The Open University

School of
HEALTH
&
SOCIAL
WELFARE

K100
Understanding Health and
Social Care

Block 6

When Care Goes Wrong

Ben Onwendine

K100 Production Team

Andrew Northedge (Chair)
Jan Walmsley (Deputy Chair)
Margaret Allott (Course Manager)
Tanya Hames (Course Secretary)
Joanna Bornat
Hilary Brown
Celia Davies
Roger Gomm
Sheila Peace
Martin Robb
Deborah Cooper (VQ Centre)

Jill Alger, Julie Fletcher (Editors); Janis Gilbert (Graphic Artist); Hannah Brunt, Rob Williams (Designers); Paul Smith (Librarian); Deborah Bywater (Project Control Assistant); Ann Carter (Print Buying Controller); Pam Berry (Text Processing Services); Mike Levers (Photographer); Vic Lockwood, Alison Tucker, Kathy Wilson (BBC Producers); Maggie Guillon (Cartoonist)

Regional Education and Training Managers

Lindsay Brigham
Anne Fletcher
Carole Ulanowsky

External Assessor

Professor Lesley Doyal, University of Bristol

This is the K100 core course team. Many other people also contributed to making the course and their names are given in the Introduction and Study Guide.

The Open University
Walton Hall, Milton Keynes MK7 6AA

First published 1998

Designed, edited and typeset by The Open University

Printed and bound in the United Kingdom by Thanet Press

ISBN 0 7492 3425 3

For further information on related Open University courses and study packs, write to The Information Officer, School of Health and Social Welfare, The Open University, Walton Hall, Milton Keynes MK7 6AA.

1.1

18109B/k100b6u22i1.1

Contents

Study skills by Andrew Northedge

Introduction

This block looks at some difficult issues in care work, when there may be conflicting views about what to do for the best and uncomfortable feelings to resolve. The block focuses on three main areas.

Unit 22 looks at times when caring presents real dilemmas and difficult decisions, especially in residential settings.

Unit 23 focuses more on personal relationships and on how to draw the line between ordinary upsets and conflicts and real abuses of power.

Unit 24 explores a policy response to abuse or malpractice and services which support people who are survivors of abuse.

Unit 25 builds on these three themes and explores how to put skills for dealing with risk and abuse into practice.

Some key issues from earlier in the course will be revisited, such as boundaries and roles, accountability and taboos around intimate care. You will also look at the organisational context within which decisions are made and practice evolves. The context includes attitudes and views held in society as a whole about our bodies, about sex and sexuality, race and ethnicity, punishment and abuse. We also have to consider not only what we believe to be right but what power people have to do anything; hence we also explore aspects of the legal framework within which the caring professions operate.

The block starts by looking at difficult areas of intimate care, control and protection and at the basis on which decisions are made in these areas. It then goes on to consider what is labelled 'abuse' and what can be done to act on behalf of people who are vulnerable or unable to protect themselves. Some of the images in the block are disturbing, but then some of the work of caring is disturbing. What this material does is to put into words things which are often dealt with by being left unsaid.

Unit 22
Difficult Decisions

Prepared for the course team by Hilary Brown

While you are working on Unit 22, you will need:
- Course Reader
- Offprints Book
- *The Good Study Guide*
- Audio Cassette 6, side 1, parts 1 and 2
- Wallchart

Contents

Introduction

In this unit we are going to look at a number of situations which put a strain on the idea that caring is just an extension of 'being ordinary'. These include times when people are giving intimate care and situations when *control* as well as *care* has to be exercised. In these special circumstances, since the normal rules do not apply, we have to develop a set of special rules to guide practice, thinking very carefully about these core questions:

Core questions

- How can boundaries be respected in situations where intimate care is being given?

- In what situations and with what safeguards are services entitled to apply sanctions or restrain someone to stop them harming themselves or another person?

- How can choices, rights and autonomy be balanced against the need to protect people in receipt of care who put themselves at risk of harm?

- When and how can systems become abusive?

The unit has four sections which focus on care, control, protection and regimes. The examples given are mostly based on the experiences of young people and adults with learning difficulties but they raise issues which apply equally to other people receiving care. The main thread is how to make decisions when care goes beyond normal social relationships and into uncharted waters.

One guiding principle of the unit is that people need safeguards once others start doing things to (or for) them which most people would not expect to have done. This is particularly so for people who are too dependent to act as partners in care relationships. Anyone cast in the role of a 'do-gooder' has considerable licence to overstep boundaries. Sobsey argues that disabled people sometimes have fewer rights than criminals:

> *Because caregivers are seen as helping people with disabilities, they are allowed to do things that would not otherwise be permitted. For example, people who are convicted criminals cannot be incarcerated indefinitely, are allowed to make an appeal and speak in their own defence: cannot have food, fluids or required medical care withheld; and cannot be placed on aversive behaviour management programmes or given psychoactive medications against their will because these things violate their rights. People with disabilities do not receive the same protection, however, because they are thought to be 'helped not punished' by these interventions.*

> *(Sobsey, 1994, p. 142)*

Under the guise of helping, a great deal of cajoling, guidance and controlling goes on, some of it quite appropriately – *some* of the people receiving care, at *some* points in their lives, may benefit from these things. But at other times services fail to be aware of the control they exert, and the lack of independent channels for challenging service decisions or actions leaves people who use services very vulnerable.

Crossing boundaries: a case study

The first core question is 'how can boundaries be respected in situations where intimate care is being given?' This will be explored through a fictional case study set in a residential unit for young people with learning (and some associated physical and sensory) difficulties. The story is fictional in the sense that I have made the characters up and put all the separate strands together but the setting is based on a real establishment and each incident or situation is based on a real event or on the experience of someone known to me through my work or personal life. The fact that it is presented as a story (like the Jim and Marianne case study in Unit 10) does not make it any less real, it merely provides anonymity for the people and services involved.

The first character you will meet is Marie, a new care assistant. In Unit 23 you will meet her neighbour Pat, who has a sister-in-law Bernice who works in a playgroup; in Unit 24 Allan, Pat's husband and Bernice's brother, who is an information and planning officer in the social services, takes over the story.

Marie

Marie is a young white woman who has recently started work at a residential unit for young people with physical and learning disabilities run by a local charity. She trained as an NNEB nurse at her local college after leaving school but did one of her placements at a day nursery which included children with learning difficulties and really enjoyed it. She was very thrilled to get this job: it is local and she can easily get there on the bus even for the early morning shift. It doesn't pay very well but it is better than being a private nanny or babysitter and she really looked forward to getting her first proper pay packet. Marie lives at home: she has been going out with her boyfriend Barry for two years and is saving up to get engaged.

Before the interview Marie was sent a prospectus about the unit, which described how it had been set up to help young people who had

Providing ordinary opportunities

left special schools to make the transition to adult living. There was also a special needs unit for people with more severe learning difficulties. The brochure said:

> We have a commitment to treating the residents here like any other young people. We provide opportunities for them to reach adulthood by making their own choices and by treating them as normal young adults would expect to be treated.

Marie was at a bit of a disadvantage in the interview because her previous experience had been with younger children. The interviewers asked her about her training and said that it would be important to treat the young people as adults and not as children. They said they were looking for someone who could act 'more like a friend than a parent'. Marie latched on to what they were saying and said she thought she could do that because she always prided herself on treating children with respect and not in a babyish way.

The head of care also asked Marie about care plans and she was able to talk about the system used at the nursery for recording what each child liked and needed during the day, such as if they had a special diet or needed a nap at a certain time, and so on. She talked about her work with Tom, a boy with Down's syndrome in whom she had taken a special interest, and how they had been working on helping him to learn new words by noticing toys he liked to play with and getting him to ask for them.

The head of care was impressed with Marie's maturity and enthusiasm and as she had a good reference from her college and from the nursery, they offered her the job. She started on the Monday after she finished college but was invited to come up for a couple of hours on Friday evening to see round the unit and to meet her 'shift', especially Joan, who was the senior care officer who would be showing her the ropes. Joan introduced her to Richard and Rachel as she was to be keyworker for them both and would be getting to know them better than the other residents.

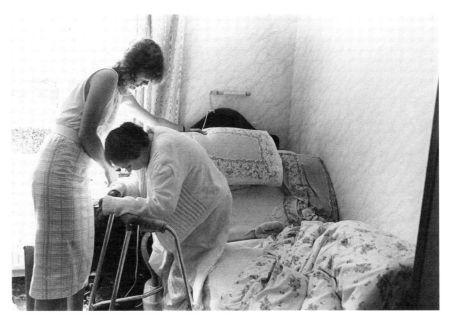

A first day at work

For the first week she was to be on day duty, which involved getting people up and ready for breakfast and then helping them into the dining-room. Understandably, she was nervous on her first day but she got there on time and worked with another member of staff to help Rachel get dressed. Rachel needed a lot of help and Marie realised as they were having breakfast that she did not know how to feed someone who needed this amount of support. She looked round for help but there was no one near who wasn't busy so she 'owned up' to Rachel, who grinned. When Marie put the food in too quickly Rachel spat it out, but gradually Marie found the right speed and relaxed and they began to get on well.

The second day began in the same way except that Marie was to get Richard up first as Rachel was having a lie in. Richard had his own room and Marie knocked and went in. Joan had said Richard was a 'total care' but Marie wasn't quite sure what that meant. She had met him briefly the day before and knew he liked to play on his computer using a probe he wore around his forehead, but she felt a bit shy of barging into his room and didn't really know where to start. She had been told that he could move from the bed to his wheelchair but would otherwise need help with dressing and toileting.

When Marie went to help Richard get up it was obvious that he had an erection. She didn't know what to do: she didn't want to embarrass him but she couldn't help blushing. She wondered if she should go out of the room or go to find Joan, but if she did find her Joan would be busy and also Marie didn't know what she would say, so she decided to stay and just turn away for a bit. Eventually she took Richard to the bathroom. By this stage she was confused as well as embarrassed. She realised that Richard was going to need help to go to the loo and saw the urinal bottles on the shelf. Since he could not use his hands she had to put his penis into the bottle and keep it there while he peed. Then she took him back to his room and helped him to wash his face and get dressed.

Marie had never seen a man's penis before: although she was going steady with Barry, they had decided to wait until they were married before they had sex, which was in keeping with their religious beliefs. She felt upset that she had not realised this would be involved in the job and when she got home she thought it best not to say anything in case Barry or her parents misunderstood. She thought Barry might tell her she should leave the job so she kept it to herself. All the other women at the centre just seemed to get on with it and she didn't want to make a fuss. When her friends asked her about her new job she talked about her trouble feeding Rachel and about her time in the art room.

If Marie had got a job in a bank or a shop she would not have been expected to take a young man of her own age to the toilet, or to see him naked. Everyone acted as if it was the most 'normal' thing in the world, but it wasn't normal in Marie's world. Over the next few months Marie came to see it as normal too: when her friend Debbie came to work at the unit after Christmas, Marie forgot to tell her what she was letting herself in for.

Section 1

Care

1.1 The strains of intimate care

As you read in Block 1, intimate care involves stepping over people's usual boundaries. It takes us out of familiar territory in terms of how we relate to each other. It necessitates *breaking* the usual rules about how to behave in order to attend to bodily functions which we normally take a lot of trouble to keep private, and this 'secrecy' extends to the work itself. A key issue in Marie's story is the assumption that this area of the work does not need to be mentioned.

Activity 1   A better induction for Marie?

Allow about 15 minutes   Consider the information you have about how Marie was introduced to the work. Then make your own notes on the following questions.

(a)   What could have been done differently in the interview or during Marie's first few days?

(b)   How could the subject have been brought up in a way which would have made Marie's introduction to the work easier and would have acknowledged that it was a difficult position to be in?

Once you have done this, jot down a short 'speech' which the head of care could have made at the end of the interview to prepare Marie for this aspect of the work. What needs to be said? How can the subject be broached in a way which leaves it open for Marie to come back if she has any problems? And what about Richard – how do you think Marie's inexperience might have affected him?

Comment   For the speech I imagined something like this:

> *You will find that the work requires you to undertake some very intimate tasks, like taking a young man to the toilet, washing parts of the body – his penis, his testicles – which most people keep private. It may worry you at first. If we appoint you, I'll make sure I'm on hand when you start work, and at the end of your shift for the first week, so that you can raise any questions you might have, and ask for advice. Managing feelings about intimate care is an important part of the job. You need to feel comfortable with it, and so do the residents, who may also feel quite sensitive about it. These young people may have disabilities, but they are also men and women, and their feelings about their bodies need to be respected.*

Now look back over Marie's story and over what you have scripted for the head of care to say to her. Did you imagine that the head of care was a woman or a man? How did this affect the way he or she spoke to Marie and what it was appropriate for him or her to say? Would it have made a difference if Marie had been an older woman do you think? Personally, I found it easier to imagine a female head of care making the speech I scripted than a male.

It might also have been different if Marie had been a young man. It is possible that if *she* was a *he*, he would not have been expected to dress or toilet a woman. As we have seen, women are expected to know how to do care work because of their previous experience in the private sphere of the family, whereas there tends to be a different set of beliefs about men doing caring work. Sometimes this includes fears that they might be less sensitive, or even abusive. In establishments like this one, men tend to do less of the actual caring work and more administration or management. These concerns help to justify this division of labour.

So we can see a number of factors at work in Marie's story:

- First, there is the issue that an important part of the work she is being expected to do has been left unspoken. It is 'taken for granted', silent and invisible. In turn this has the effect that Marie does not feel able to ask for help and actively colludes in keeping the silence around it by not telling her boyfriend or family, and by not passing on her experience to her friend who later joins her in the work. Marie learns that what is expected of her is to do the work without commenting on it.

- Second, Marie doesn't know *how* to do this aspect of the work in a sensitive way, without embarrassing Richard or making him feel awkward. She has to manage this part of the work so that she can also relate to Richard as his keyworker – and she hardly knows him!

- Third, we can see that this aspect of the work has something to do with gender because the rules are different according to whether the people concerned are male or female. Because Marie is a woman it is as if she is expected to know how to do these tasks without being told: because it is 'women's work'.

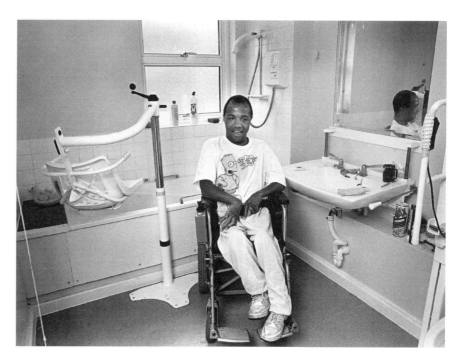

Unacknowledged tasks

- Lastly, we can see that the issue of intimate care cuts across the formal culture of the workplace. Marie is given information about what her job entails in a formal interview. This may have been conducted according to agreed rules designed, for example, to ensure equal opportunities. There is a job description which sets out the main requirements of the job (but which doesn't include taking people to the toilet) and a person specification (which doesn't say anything about it either). The personnel officer has not deliberately missed out these aspects of the work, but consigned them to a different space. They are part of a private sphere even within the workplace, not part of the publicly acknowledged aspects of the job.

Marie does not get induction, instruction or supervision in how to do them, and they are not part of the management relationship. Especially if her manager is a man, Marie will not expect him to go into detail about how this part of her work should be performed, whereas for other parts of her job, such as how to fill in a care plan or draw up a teaching programme, he may show her what to do or assess her competence and give her feedback on how well she is doing.

It is almost as if Marie has taken on two jobs, one which is publicly acknowledged and accounted for (her professional role) and the other which takes place behind the scenes, which she has to manage privately. This sometimes causes problems as it did, for example, in Marie's third week in the job when she was told off by her manager because she was late for a meeting with Richard's social worker and speech therapist. The reason for her delay was that she was helping to clean someone up after an 'accident' in the toilet. Marie's workload is often discussed as if these private elements of it do not take up any space or time. Actually they have to take priority over the written and administrative functions but that is not openly acknowledged. Writing about nursing, Lawler (whose work you came across in Unit 4) comments that:

> *Nursing involves not only doing things which are traditionally assigned to females, and learning to do them by experience and practice, but also crossing social boundaries, breaking taboos and doing things for people which they would normally do for themselves in private if they were able.*

(Lawler, 1991, p. 30)

Key points

- Intimate care is not 'ordinary'. It presents a very unusual set of dilemmas for both the carer and the person cared for.

- Despite how 'extra-ordinary' such tasks are, care workers are often expected to be able to do this side of the work 'naturally'.

- Expectations about intimate care and caring are different for men and women staff and service users.

- Although care establishments are largely organised around the need to provide intimate care, this may not be acknowledged in the public face of the service, or reflected in its training, guidance or supervision.

1.2 Silences and concealment

Anthropologists and psychoanalysts use the term 'taboo' to describe forbidden activities, feelings or relationships. All societies seem to have particular rules and rituals to deal with bodily functions, sexuality and death, sometimes expressed in terms of hygiene or religion, and these keep them separated off from everyday life. When social rules function well they are invisible. We only notice them when we have committed a *faux pas* and caused embarrassment. Marie very quickly and correctly learnt the rules in this establishment: from the lack of acknowledgement of this aspect of the job she picked up that it was not an oversight that no one had spoken about it. It was *not to be* spoken about. In another care home down the road a friend of Marie's complained to the proprietor that one of the (male) residents tried to grab her in a sexual way. He told her quite sharply that 'if she couldn't stand the heat she should get out of the kitchen'. In other words, she was being told not to complain and that her only option, if she didn't like it, was to leave. She found she was working in an occupational subculture where only certain things are permitted to be discussed (like the auxiliaries working in Cedar Court whom you met in Unit 4).

This kind of silence tends to be produced when there are hierarchies in which tasks are delegated to some people rather than others. Dealing with intimate care tends to be a low-status task. It is often referred to as 'basic' care as opposed to the more technical tasks within nursing and the planning, educational or therapeutic tasks within residential services. In Unit 4 it was referred to as 'backstage work', following Goffman. Hughes, another sociologist, writing in 1971 coined the term 'dirty work', which is the work within any society or profession which is delegated downwards and/or concealed (Hughes, 1971). Caring for people's bodies could be regarded as the 'dirty work' of care, as well as 'backstage' work.

While nurses are taught procedures for carrying out personal care tasks, they are rarely explicitly 'taught' how to deal with the emotions these tasks occasion. Learning 'on the job' produces a kind of knowledge based on practice rather than theory which is literally difficult to put into words. This helps to keep the work and the skills it involves invisible.

1.3 Women's work

Gender and power play a role in keeping issues like this out of the public arena. One reason for women's comparative silence in our culture is that more of what they do is defined as 'private' or 'personal'. Things they talk about are often downgraded – being deemed unimportant, boring or inappropriate. When large and difficult areas of experience are left out of public discussion we need to ask why. Ignoring the experience of certain groups of people is a way of exercising power over them. It allows their points of view and their needs to slip off the agenda. Women and members of minority ethnic groups have protested against being treated in this way. But it is an experience shared by carers and users of services (Pascall, 1986 p. 30, and Brown and Smith, 1989, p. 108 make this link).

Beyond the fact that women have tasks to do which are defined as not worth discussing, is the fact that women do seem to be given roles in dealing with and containing feelings, and particularly sexual feelings. This is true in care settings and also in other work such as shop work where 'the customer is always right', or in a reception where the receptionist is always welcoming and on display. Women workers often have to manage the way they present themselves and control their emotional reactions. This is particularly so in care work, when they are dealing with intimate or intrusive procedures. We introduced the idea of 'emotional labour' (Hochschild, 1983) in Unit 4, Section 6. It is hard work, partly because it is not made explicit or rewarded. In fact, you only see it is part of the expectations of the job if you stop doing it. Hochschild's work was with air hostesses, who have to put on a brave (and usually very well made up) face and be 'nice' to passengers no matter how obnoxious they are back. Similarly, carers have to be open to all the people in their care whether or not they 'like' them or find them easy to look after. If 'the customer is always right', it makes it very difficult to know when you *can* draw the line, for example in relation to sexual or racial harassment from users. If the customer is always right it is often at the expense of women workers.

1.4 Distance and closeness

A lot of emotional labour is concerned with getting the right balance between being close, friendly and warm, and maintaining a proper distance. Lawler writes about learning emotional control by sticking to a set procedure and cultivating an 'air of detachment' (1991, p. 126). In terms of care work it is never quite clear which side to err on – being too cold would be seen as unprofessional, but so is being too familiar. (Remember the dilemmas about drawing boundaries that the home carers in the Unit 3 audio cassette faced?)

Activity 2   **Learning to manage embarrassing situations**

Allow about 45 minutes

Now read Chapter 26 in the Reader in which Lawler discusses the way nurses learn to manage their embarrassment and the discomfort of their patients. While you are reading, jot down some notes relating each section of the chapter to your own experiences.

Here are some pointers to help you.

- The chapter starts by describing the background of the nurses Lawler interviewed in this study. If you do caring work, either in a paid or unpaid capacity, how do you think your own background has equipped you? Has it helped or made it more difficult for you to be comfortable around other people's bodies and bodily functions? If you need help with intimate care yourself, has this been made more or less embarrassing for you as a result of the way you were brought up?

- The nurses interviewed all have particular stories to tell about their *first* bed-baths, dead bodies and so on. Do you have any particularly vivid experiences like this relating to your own initial experiences of caring or being cared for?

- Have you ever been in hospital or had any intimate procedure carried out like this? Did it help you if you had a sense of the nurse following a set procedure, or would you rather they had asked you how you wanted something done, or how you would have done it yourself? If you are a carer, do you have a routine? Does it help you? Do you think it makes things less embarrassing for other people?

- If you are, or have been, a carer, have you learnt to switch off your emotions or do you sometimes find things harrowing, disgusting or unpleasant? What do you do then? Do you pretend, or do you avoid the person who needs your help? If you are on the receiving end of care, do you like your carer to keep their distance or do you prefer more of the human touch?

- Language is mentioned because that is a particular stumbling block when it comes to discussing bodily functions or sexuality. What kind of vocabulary do you feel most comfortable using at home – or at work? For example, children have their own vocabulary of 'wees' and 'poohs' while other people may use medical terminology.

Comment   You probably came up with some very personal anecdotes in response to
this activity. Keep these in mind as we explore why these areas are so
difficult.

In the Reader Lawler describes the context in which nurses work as a
'social vacuum'. Care workers like Marie often have even less structure.
They may have no induction, no uniform, no set procedures, no medical
ethos and no fixed standards to protect them. Their role is not one other
people recognise. They may be called something quite vague like a
'support worker' or a 'house companion'. When they are not providing
physical care they are supposed to act as a friend or equal to the person
they are caring for, which means they have to switch in and out of roles
and vary the distance between them as they perform different aspects of
their work. They also have to maintain this very responsive personal
touch even when they are responsible for looking after a group of
people whose needs have to be juggled and balanced.

When people make decisions in this kind of environment there are no
clear markers and after a while there is a tendency to forget what the
normal rules are. A recent study explored how women care staff
manage distance around the sexuality of men with learning difficulties.
It describes:

> *... how acutely aware some women staff are of the contradictions within
> their role ... when it comes to performing their caring responsibilities
> without compounding the risk of sexual harassment from their male
> clients.*
>
> *(Thompson et al., 1997, p. 574)*

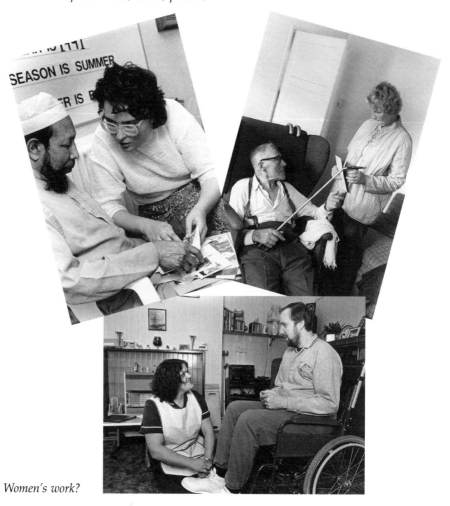

Women's work?

Walking the tightrope between being too distant and too familiar, several women acknowledged the double messages they give out to the men they care for. For example, one woman said she wouldn't be this nice to any other man unless she was going to have a sexual relationship with him. Here we see that the expectations of her role as a carer cut across the way a woman of her age would normally expect to behave with men, leaving her, and her clients, confused. To continue Marie's story, later in the year Richard developed quite a crush on her, which she handled by telling him emphatically about her boyfriend Barry. In Thompson *et al.*'s study this was described as a common strategy and one way of re-establishing distance.

The paper by Thompson *et al.* also considers the organisational context within which much care work takes place: a predominantly female workforce with men occupying management roles. They describe the lack of support from managers and the unspoken expectation that women will *cope with* this aspect of the work, on their own. If a man service user misunderstands, the woman carer is invited to think it is her fault and something she should get right herself, not a function of the situation she has been put in. Even when the sexual behaviour of service users is seriously outside what any other women would expect to deal with at work, it is played down and not taken seriously. The authors comment on:

> ... the differential power which men and women staff hold within their organisations to frame behaviour such as this as a 'problem' rather than to see it subsumed as a routine part of the work.
>
> (Thompson et al., 1997, p. 580)

We have so far considered the issue of boundaries from the point of view of paid carers. Doing intimate things for someone you *do* know and have an ongoing relationship with can be just as difficult to manage. We saw in Unit 1 that Lynne shied away from taking on intimate care of her father. Oliver (1983) writes about the experiences of wives caring for disabled husbands. She tells how wives are expected to take on the role of carer with little help. Their presence and assumed willingness to care often lead to their husbands being discharged earlier from hospital and sent home with fewer aids or support services than a single person would have, or than a woman being cared for by her male partner. Rather than being treated as a person in her own right, 'the wife' is not able to negotiate what she will and will not do. Oliver writes of one woman who despite being:

> ... extremely distressed by the very intimate tasks she now had to do for her husband, like wiping his bottom, was told by the examining doctor [when she applied for attendance allowance] that what she was doing was 'no more than any wife should'. She broke down completely when the doctor left, and when her husband's application was turned down, forbade him to appeal, in order that she should not be put through such a humiliating ordeal again.
>
> (Oliver, 1983, p. 77)

In this case embarrassment had a real financial as well as an emotional cost. Crossing boundaries is also an issue for men who take on the role of 'carer'; for example, a father might find himself coming into contact with his disabled daughter's menstruation in a way other fathers would not. Family members and care workers find themselves being asked to stretch to meet an ideal no matter how pressed they are or how unrealistic the expectations on them.

> **Key points**
>
> - Intimate care is seen as both 'low status' and 'women's work' (not a coincidence).
>
> - 'Emotional labour' is more than just managing emotions. It refers to the work of maintaining at least the fiction of a close, supportive role in a relationship which is not reciprocal.
>
> - Care workers are constantly crossing and rebuilding boundaries: hence the tension between closeness and distance in their relationships with service users.
>
> - The lack of clear boundaries presents problems in relation to sexual behaviour as well as to intimate care.

1.5 Developing agreed ways of working

Although it may be undesirable to cut across the informality of care relationships by making unnecessary rules or regulations, intimate care is clearly one site where things can go wrong. There is a narrow margin of error. The usual social rules and inhibitions have already been broken and it is not always easy to arrive at new ones which are appropriate to the particular context within which you are caring or being cared for. Moreover, receiving or giving care arouses strong feelings which people rarely put into words.

Activity 3   **Help with going to the toilet**

Allow about 10 minutes   Imagine that you need help to go to the toilet. Perhaps you do receive this kind of assistance, or have done in the past. If so, you will have first-hand knowledge to draw on. Write down three things which your helper could do to ease any embarrassment or discomfort you might feel, and three things which would make the whole situation even worse. Think about who would be helping you in this situation, their gender, their relationship to you, their manner, what they say, their facial expression, and so on.

Comment   You might have included things like:

- what tone you would like them to take with you

- whether you would want them to talk while they were helping you

- whether you would like them to pretend they haven't really noticed what is going on.

Lawler's research identified the following 'scene-defining' strategies (remember Unit 4) employed by doctors and nurses when undertaking intimate care:

- They set up the caring task by making clear that the context is 'medical' rather than social or sexual.

- They use their uniform as 'a barrier'.

- They put on a deliberately matter-of-fact manner.

- They protect the person's privacy by sending other people away or drawing curtains.

- They say things which minimise the awkwardness like 'Oh, it isn't much', 'It isn't that bad', or 'It could have happened to anyone'.
- They change the style, volume and tone of their conversation to create a private atmosphere.

'Intimate' care?

But still nurses have to deal with their own natural reactions especially around smell, which can be particularly difficult to 'stomach'. Here they will develop ways of concentrating on the mechanics of the task, or they may take breaks by going out of the room. One of the nurses Lawler interviewed said she 'hides the horribleness from the patient' (p. 176). It is as if the worker becomes more formal to compensate for the very personal and potentially intrusive nature of the help they are giving. But this might not be appropriate if this help is being given at home or in a homelike setting.

So what can be done to help carers or people being cared for in these situations? One approach is to bring the subject of intimate care 'out of the bathroom', so to speak, and on to the job description. This has benefits for workers and management: it allows this part of the work, its difficulty and delicacy, to be acknowledged, but it also makes managers take back responsibility for how it should be done. Some services have begun to explore just what good practice would mean in these areas as an alternative to waiting until things go wrong and then saying something. For example Eric, who is a colleague of Marie's, always leaves the door open a bit when he takes service users to the toilet: anyone passing by can see that he is in there with someone. The staff are now having a discussion about whether it should be shut and, if so, locked or not. Eric says he is 'covering his back' but some people were saying that Eric is not doing his job properly. He can reasonably say that he does not know what 'properly' means until the staff group make up their minds.

Activity 4 Guidelines for intimate care

Allow about 10 minutes Imagine you are the head of care at Marie's unit and you are asked to draw up some rules on how to give intimate care which would act as a safeguard for the residents and also for the staff. See if you can sketch out the section on bathing residents.

Comment   Did you think about the following issues in drawing up your 'practice guidance'?

- Who should give baths, what gender, and should there be one person only or two?

- Should doors be shut and locked?

- What exactly does 'bathing' involve? What needs to be washed and how?

- How will help be given? Should staff do the bathing or try to help the residents do it for themselves?

- What *don't* you expect to happen?

Key points

- Workers providing intimate care emphasise the formality of their roles to compensate for the crossing of boundaries.

- It is difficult to hold workers to account for intimate care tasks when no one has spelt out how they want these to be done.

- Agreed procedures provide one 'benchmark' for good practice which can protect service users, staff and workers.

1.6 Unofficial work cultures

The whole issue of bodily care and bodily functions tends to be driven underground and then emerges in jokes or crudeness. Picture this scene, a few months after Marie has started, when she has become more settled within the care team.

It was quite late on a Saturday night and a group of the younger staff were sitting in the staffroom waiting for Jenny's boyfriend. He was going to give some of them a lift to the pub and the plan was for them to meet up with friends for a few drinks and then go for a curry. Marie was a bit late because she had been getting Richard ready for bed and he had had an 'accident' so she had to wash him and change his pyjamas. She rushed in after the others had already finished their handover meeting with the night staff. When she came in and mumbled about having to change Richard's pyjamas, Jenny started giggling and said it must have taken ages because he was so 'well hung'. Everybody laughed. If you had played back a video of the scene you would have seen that Marie froze for almost half a minute before she started laughing as well.

Activity 5 Joking apart ...

Allow about 10 minutes

What do you think was going through Marie's mind in that 30 seconds? Draw some thought balloons to script what she might have been saying to herself.

Comment

I think Marie might have had quite a struggle because my guess is that she disapproves of this kind of language. She may also have felt disloyal to Richard as a person she respects, and have felt uncomfortable about what could be racist undertones because Richard is black. But perhaps she also found it quite a relief to get some of her feelings out of her system before she went home. Perhaps it helped her to put work, with its peculiar rules and relationships, out of her mind so she could go back to an ordinary Saturday night out with her mates.

My first reaction to Marie and her friends was very disapproving but then I thought that maybe laughing was therapeutic. You have probably heard of 'a Freudian slip'. Although we try constantly to censor what we say, forbidden thoughts and secrets tend to leak out in the form of jokes, mistakes or slips.

Another reaction I had was to think how difficult it would have been for Marie *not* to laugh. Getting on well at work depends on going along with what other people do and fitting into the 'culture' of the place. Different workplaces develop their own jokes and jargon. Perhaps laughing about people's bodies and sexuality is one way Marie and her colleagues 'let off steam' about being exposed to the intimacy of people's bodies.

Isabel Menzies carried Freud's thinking a bit further in a classic piece of work on nursing practice called *The Functioning of Social Systems as a Defence Against Anxiety* (Menzies, 1970). She said that it was not only individuals who have an 'unconscious', but organisations and whole professions. The informal culture (the jokes, the language and also the way jobs are set up) is partly a consequence of the need to be defended from some of the things they are dealing with. For example, if you were an undertaker you couldn't get upset about every individual whose funeral you arranged. For your own sanity you'd have to distance yourself. Probably there are all kinds of 'corpse jokes' which take the sting out of the work.

A nurse I know who works on an oncology ward told me the joke about cancer being safe from 'cut-backs' in her hospital because it was a 'growth area'. Remember the nurse in Reader Chapter 26 who, with her fellow trainee, became 'hysterical with laughter' when she encountered her first death, but who then became 'sad because we hadn't witnessed anything like this before'.

Think back too to Unit 4 and Lee-Treweek's account of the 'bedroom world' at Cedar Court, where the staff made jokes about the patients' impairments which denied their feelings and needs. Was this worse than the episode in Marie's home? At least Richard was not present and aware of what was being said. Or perhaps once you start making jokes you can't draw a neat line which stops you from passing on some of the cruelty to those receiving care?

Key points

- Jokes may be used as a way of 'letting off steam' about the strains of care work.

- Aspects of the work which are not publicly acknowledged tend to get dealt with in the informal culture of the establishment or work group: open supervision or discussion may avoid this.

1.7 Establishing boundaries

Activity 6   **Managing the hidden culture**

Allow about 15 minutes   Imagine now that you are Marie's manager and you decide to call in at the unit on your way back from a day out. You often drop in unannounced to make sure everything is OK and because it is the only chance you get to talk to some of the night staff. You walk in on the joke-telling incident and hear from the corridor what has been said. What do you do?

(a)   Go in and join in the laughter.

(b)   Go in and confront the staff – if so what exactly would you say?

(c)   Turn around and pretend you didn't hear.

(d)   Decide not to challenge the staff now but to put on some staff training at a later date.

Now write a paragraph saying why you decided to tackle it this way. What went through your mind? If you decided not to intervene, think about how much worse it would have to get before you did go in and say something.

Comment   Managers clearly have a role to play in containing these aspects of the work: acknowledging difficult issues, setting agreed limits on how tasks should be approached, and helping individual staff to walk the tightrope of not being too cut off or too close to those they are working with. If Marie's manager joined in, or even initiated the joking, there would be no containment and nothing to stop things getting worse. It is up to the manager, or occasionally inspectors, to set out what is expected and then monitor whether staff keep within agreed boundaries.

Intimate care is an area in which boundaries are almost inevitably crossed but it is by no means the only area in which a spontaneous response can have unforeseen implications. We have talked a lot about the boundaries of care relationships in Units 3 and 4 and again in this unit. Now we look at a real-life attempt at establishing such boundaries. Enfield Social Services (1996) has drawn up guidelines on professional boundaries for a wide range of staff including field social workers and those working in residential care. The guidelines attempt to set markers on a range of issues in professional relationships with children and adults. In particular they cover issues about:

- not taking advantage of clients (e.g. in sexual or financial transactions)

- disclosure of personal information within professional relationships

- expressing affection in worker–client relationships.

Activity 7   Guidance on professional boundaries

Allow about 30 minutes

Listen to Audio Cassette 6, side 1, part 1 now. You will hear Vicky Golding, an Area Manager for Enfield Social Services, describing why her department decided to develop these guidelines and talking about some of the controversial areas in the guidelines and what it means to be 'professional'.

As you listen to the tape jot down anything you react strongly to.

Then look through the guidelines in Offprint 31 and note down which items you agree with and which you would not want to be bound by in your own situation. If you are on the receiving end of care, think about whether you would want this kind of 'professional' relationship with your carer or if you expect them to be more open and personal with you.

Comment   The guidelines in Offprint 31 grew out of two situations in which workers had 'overstepped boundaries' by taking individual children home, but they cover the more general issue of where to set limits in professional relationships in terms of how much personal disclosure and expression of affection is ever appropriate in a professional relationship. The model of professionalism represented here is one which errs on the side of maintaining a certain distance. Did you agree with this, or would you have drawn the line at a different point?

One of the controversial areas is just how much we expect workers to reveal of themselves. The Enfield Social Services guidelines suggest that workers should not reveal much about their personal lives to their clients but this can also create difficulties. For example, Marie told Richard about her boyfriend Barry as one way of re-establishing some distance when he was interpreting their relationship on a more personal level. Another exception might be that a gay worker at Marie's unit might be able to provide a very positive role model to gay or lesbian young people if they were allowed to be open about their sexuality. Vicky Golding drew a distinction between the kind of reciprocal sharing which goes on in a self-help group where one's personal experience would be seen as an asset in the work, and the more anonymous role of a care worker or social worker. Do you agree with this distinction?

Another difficult area addressed in the guidelines is the expression of affection and touch, which would be considered quite normal for children if they were being cared for within their families; kissing and hugging, saying 'I love you' and so on were also singled out as issues in services for older people and people with learning difficulties. It might be different for service users who get affection from other relationships in their lives than for people who are isolated and otherwise deprived of any such contact. What do you think? The guidelines also address the issue of favouritism; for example, if one resident is given gifts or taken out more than others in a group care setting.

Actions are 'graded' in the guidelines so that some are forbidden altogether, such as having sex with a client, others are subject to a manager's discretion and others are up to workers to decide for themselves. Did you find this helpful? Craft and Brown (1994) highlight the importance of guidance which works to 'define the greatest possible leeway within which individual workers and teams can reach their own decisions' (p. 18) and which balance these two functions:

> ... to draw some acceptable boundary around the personal and the professional and to define the boundaries within which individual workers can respond as they think best.
>
> (Craft and Brown, 1994, p. 18)

If the young male care worker in Unit 3 who led Lynne to imagine he felt genuine affection for her had had access to such guidelines *before* starting work, do you think it might have prevented him from making the mistakes he did?

The open consultation which has taken place in Enfield Social Services goes to the heart of what social and care services are about. Are social workers or care staff there to replicate ordinary relationships, to compensate for a lack of them, or to provide practical help while staying in the background so that people can 'live their own lives'? We saw in Unit 3, Section 5, that disabled people want assistance without strings attached, and that 'care', despite its friendly overtones, can be more of a hindrance than a help. But some clients may rely on professional carers to provide them with affection and social contact which they do not get elsewhere. The answer is bound to vary for different people and different settings, but the process of consulting with a wide range of people and attempting to provide some clarity is an important one for clients, staff and managers.

Vicky Golding emphasised that 'professional boundaries' are important for service users who:

> are often very vulnerable – they can be needy and boundary-less themselves and open to exploitation by a worker in a powerful position ...

But she also points out their usefulness as a framework for managers because they:

> clarify what is acceptable and so where a boundary has been breached, we can actually point to it and use [the guidelines] as a management tool ...

and for workers:

> *but they are also for protecting the worker, which is really important because workers are vulnerable and don't always realise how they're leaving themselves open.*

This reflects the triangular nature of accountability which you read about in Block 5.

Key points

- Managers need to 'contain' difficult areas of care work.
- Boundaries are not only crossed in intimate care but in 'social' settings as well.
- Professional relationships are different from ordinary reciprocal friendships.
- Formal guidance provides a reference point which can protect service users, staff and managers.

Section 2
Control

So far in this unit we have focused on intimate care because it is one arena within which workers find themselves doing things which go well beyond normal social relationships and rules. We have seen the tension which can arise if no distinction is made between personal and professional approaches to care work and we have considered how to manage the tension between being warm/personal and distant/professional within the same relationship. I will now examine another area of care where the usual rules just do not apply: caring relationships which include a measure of control, containment and sanctions.

At the unit where Marie works there are a number of young people who have multiple problems. Rosalie is one such young woman. She has a hearing impairment, difficulties in communicating and severe learning difficulties, and is often aggressive to staff or other residents when things get too much for her. During Marie's second week there was a staff meeting at which Rosalie was the main subject of discussion. It appeared that she had lashed out at one of the instructors and broken her nose: the instructor was now off sick and there was a lot of sympathy for her. The staff were angry and saying, 'this time things have gone too far'. Some people were angry with Rosalie but others seemed to be directing their feelings at the management. Some staff were saying they shouldn't have to work with someone like Rosalie and that this place wasn't equipped to deal with people who are as 'severe' as she is. They wanted her to be removed. The management were saying that she should be allowed to stay with some extra support put in place and they had invited a psychologist along to discuss with staff how best to respond to what she called Rosalie's 'challenging behaviour'.

Marie doesn't really know Rosalie but she felt a bit alarmed: mostly she just listened to the meeting and she noticed that Rosalie's keyworker was undecided: he thought that if Rosalie was allowed to get away with this she would just do it again, but on the other hand he had worked hard to keep her in the unit for the last six months and he didn't want to give up yet. Marie shared his ambivalence.

This situation is not unlike many which crop up in the context of children's and young people's services but in this context it appears that Rosalie's behaviour is complicated by her specific learning difficulties.

2.1 Different ways of talking about difficult behaviour

Although the staff group came together to discuss how to respond to Rosalie's behaviour, you might have noticed that they approached it from very different perspectives. As the meeting progressed they even used different words. You could say they were speaking within different 'discourses'.

If you had been a fly on the wall, for the rest of the staff meeting you would have seen that these discourses were signalled in various ways.

First, the ways in which they *described* Rosalie's behaviour were very different:

- assault
- lashed out
- challenging behaviour
- had a tantrum
- went mad.

Second, they *explained* it in different terms including:

- frustration
- trying to get her own way
- her mother has 'spoiled' her
- communication difficulties
- attention seeking.

Different ways of talking about the problem lead to different answers ...

Lastly, they had different models in mind about what kind of *response* would be appropriate.

- She shouldn't be allowed to 'get away with it'.
- We should look at giving her extra help with signing.
- She should be excluded from the unit.
- She should have counselling.
- A more detailed behavioural assessment should be done.
- She should be ignored when she behaves like this in future.
- She should be treated consistently.
- If we reward her behaviour she will do it again.

It would clearly be hard to develop a consistent approach to Rosalie's difficult behaviour if everyone has a different way of talking about it, a different view of what has caused it and a different model of how to respond. You might find it useful to think of the manager's task as helping people to communicate across the gulfs signalled by these different ways of talking and thinking about the problem.

Activity 8   Behaviour speak

Allow about 5 minutes   Look back over the terms people used to describe, explain and respond to Rosalie's behaviour. Circle the ones which you would be most likely to use yourself and put a line through those which you feel sure you would not have said if you had been at the meeting.

Comment   I think I might have said that she 'lashed out' but I don't know if I would have put this down to communication difficulties or to frustration. Some staff were drawing on ways of talking they had learnt through bringing up children, using the idea of a 'tantrum', reminiscent of the 'terrible twos' stage of development. Someone else had a more adult, but almost criminal interpretation by labelling the behaviour as 'an assault'. Someone else suggested that Rosalie had lost control, 'gone mad', which brings in the idea of mental illness or imbalance.

I think that if I had to work with her I might be expressing concern about her staying at the unit unless I could see definite improvements coming as the result of an assessment or a programme. What did you think?

> **Study skills: Using different discourses**
>
> When we speak to each other we have to use a shared language. But there is more to it than that. We also have to use shared ideas, knowledge, assumptions and ways of arguing; otherwise we would not be able to make sense to each other. We can sum this up as using a shared 'discourse'. Discourses spring up between all groups of people who regularly communicate with each other. There are, for example, discourses of playground talk between children. I say 'discourses' rather than 'discourse', because younger children and older children tend to talk about different kinds of things and in different ways. Also, there are varieties of 'boy talk' and 'girl talk'. Similarly, as you move between different groups of people as an adult you take part in 'street talk', 'work talk', 'hobby talk', 'close friend talk', and so on. Without noticing you adjust what you talk about, the words you use, the jokes you tell and so on, as you move from one type of discourse to another.

In a similar way there are front-line-carer discourses, medical discourses, social work discourses, management discourses, legal discourses and so on, all connected with the world of caring. These are all ways of making sense of different aspects of caring. But they are also different ways of making sense of any particular aspect of care. For example, a decision to change policy on discharging patients from hospital would be discussed quite differently within each of these discourses. The sense we make of the world depends a lot on what discourse we bring into play when we talk about it.

In a way, what you are doing by studying K100 is acquiring a new kind of discourse. You already knew a lot about care through your own experience (we all do), but by studying K100 you are gaining access to new ways of talking (and thinking) about care. You become able to make sense of care issues in new ways by taking advantage of discourses developed through academic research and writing and through professional practice. That is why writing essays is an important part of the course – and why it is important to write in your own words, while also using ideas and ways of arguing drawn from the course. You are getting practice in saying meaningful things about care using the discourses built up by experts in the field. Your aim as a student is to become fluent in a range of discourses relevant to care. Then you will be in a position to participate in debates and decision making across the field.

When the psychologist used the term 'challenging behaviour', she was drawing on a 'professional' discourse, this time derived from psychology (Emerson *et al.*, 1987). She was brought in specially: she was not there when the incident took place and does not have to deal with Rosalie on a day-to-day basis. Is her label more accurate? More useful? More respectful to Rosalie?

As a 'professional' term, 'challenging behaviour' is a relatively new label which replaced the term 'problem' or 'difficult' behaviour. Lowe and Felce (1995) discuss this kind of shift as part of 'the general movement to use more respectful, less deficiency or problem-oriented language' (p. 118). But they go on to explain that it also conveys:

> *... something particular about how challenging behaviour should be viewed. The nature of the challenge was not a one-way affair but was a shared, or mutual, responsibility ...*

and they conclude that:

> *The change in terminology served to point up the onus on services to understand and help the individual.*
>
> *(Lowe and Felce, 1995, p. 118)*

It is like saying, 'it isn't Rosalie's problem, it's the service's problem'. The labels we attach to people act as markers saying, 'treat this person a bit differently' or 'watch out, you can't expect him or her to do this or that'.

2.2 Are labels ever helpful?

Many people think that changes in language to terms such as 'learning disability' from 'mental handicap', or 'challenging behaviour' from 'problem behaviour' mark a steady progress as people have become more willing to include people with disabilities into the mainstream: hence such terms are often referred to as 'inclusive language'. The impetus for some of these changes came from a group of sociologists called 'labelling theorists' who pointed out that labels could create an unhelpful self-fulfilling prophecy. But others have questioned whether there isn't also something a bit defensive and confusing about changing the words every few years, or if it doesn't sometimes play down real problems. Valerie Sinason (a psychoanalyst) sees language change as a way of shying away from difficult or painful issues. Writing about people with learning difficulties, she says:

> No human group has been forced to change its name so frequently. The sick and the poor are always with us, in physical presence and in verbal terms, but not the handicapped. What we are looking at is a process of euphemism. Euphemisms, linguistically, are words brought in to replace the verbal bedlinen when a particular word feels too raw, too near a disturbing experience.

(Sinason, 1992, p. 40)

Do you agree with this 'bedlinen' image?

I think that labels *can* be useful if they *alert* people to special considerations, rather than *impose* differentness, and if they send respectful but accurate signals about how we should work with someone. My neighbour's son, for example, has dyslexia and found it quite a relief to have a word to explain his difficulties: on the basis of this he is now given extra help and will have extra time in his examinations. He isn't called lazy or untidy or sloppy, or any of the other judgmental terms which have been thrown his way in the past because of his perceptual problems. Sometimes making judgments on the basis of 'normality' leads us in the wrong direction. It leads us to make moral pronouncements about people and their intentions which are not justified.

So we might question whether Marie's managers should be saying that the staff should treat residents 'as if they are normal'. If they do so, she and her colleagues have every right to feel angry and punitive towards Rosalie for hurting her instructor. Perhaps they should instead be saying something like, 'You are doing this job because Rosalie and people like her are different; they *can't* take the same responsibility as other people of their age. You need to take some of the responsibility that they can't manage on their own'. And the same might be true of other service users, including those who tend to be more blamed than helped, such as young people who have been in trouble with the courts. That is just a different kind of challenge.

Key points

- How you understand a person's behaviour will depend on the discourse you bring into play when you speak about it.

- The term 'challenging behaviour' has been introduced to shift responsibility for managing difficult behaviour from the individual to the service.

2.3 Responding to challenging behaviour

So the 'challenging behaviour' label raises the question, 'is Rosalie *responsible* for her behaviour or not?' Should she be treated *as if* she is responsible for her behaviour and punished or held to account in some way, or should the staff take responsibility for 'managing' her behaviour to stop her harming anyone else.

Activity 9	**Responding to Rosalie's behaviour**
Allow about 10 minutes	In this activity you are going to work out a way of assessing just how responsible Rosalie is. What information would you want to have to hand in order to make up your mind?
	List 10 things you would want to know more about if you were an expert being called in to help the staff respond to Rosalie.

Comment Here are some ideas.

1   Is there a pattern to Rosalie's behaviour?

2   Do some people provoke Rosalie more than others?

3   Are there particular times of day when she behaves in this way?

4   Are there certain places which seem to trigger her outbursts?

5   Does she have any dietary needs which are not being attended to?

6   What drugs is she taking, and do they have side effects?

7   When did this type of behaviour start, or has it always been present?

8   How is the behaviour handled?

9   Is there a consistent policy for managing her?

10   Have the views of people close to her (family, friends outside the unit) been sought? If so, what did they say?

Activity 10	**Understanding challenging behaviour**
Allow about 20 minutes	Now listen to Audio Cassette 6, side 1, part 2, which features Anthea Sperlinger, a consultant clinical psychologist who works with people with learning difficulties, and Chad Botley, a manager of residential services, who both get called in to respond to this kind of situation. On the tape they discuss the approach they would take to help staff work with Rosalie. As you listen, write down some answers to these questions:

(a)   What words or phrases does Anthea Sperlinger use to explain challenging behaviour?

(b)   What do carers most often assume to be the purpose of 'challenging behaviour'?

(c)   What other explanations are there for challenging behaviour?

Comment   (a)   Anthea says that 'the starting point is that all behaviour happens because there's a reason for it ... if Rosalie was able to ask nicely ... to say whatever is going on, she wouldn't need to behave in a challenging way.'

(b)   Carers often assume that if someone with learning difficulties does something antisocial, it is because they want attention, but as Anthea

Sperlinger says, there is nothing *wrong* with seeking attention and it doesn't explain all behaviour.

(c)   Anthea offers some alternative explanations which include pain, hunger, thirst, being asked to do something which is too difficult, not understanding the concept of time, being bored, possible hearing problems and lack of verbal communication.

Especially when people do not have much language we can see difficult behaviours as a way of communicating, of making things happen, or stopping things from happening. All behaviours are learnt and they usually achieve something for people. People may resort to challenging behaviour because they want you to go away or stop making demands on them. But these ideas are not only helpful in relation to people with learning difficulties: they are universal and could be applied equally to domestic violence, truancy, problem drinking, and so on.

Finding the 'function' of a behaviour, in other words what it does for the person in that particular setting or relationship, is an important first step in helping the person to change it. A psychologist like Anthea Sperlinger would usually start by asking staff to observe and record Rosalie's behaviour and to note any other times when she gets aggressive. They might use a form called an *abc* chart (or a similar assessment format), which notes what happened before an outburst (the antecedent – A), what happened during the incident (the behaviour – B) and then what happened afterwards (the consequence – C). Aggression does not always mean the same thing. For Rosalie it may be the only way she knows of saying 'stop' or controlling what happens around her: for someone else it might be the way they get staff to take notice of them or to take them to their room.

Once an assessment has focused on what the behaviour is *for*, staff can figure out how to deal with it. Anthea uses the phrase 'very vigilant and good detectives' to describe the staff's role, which requires them to stand back from the immediate situation and not react personally. In this case, if we had a video camera and could look back over the incident with the instructor, we would see that she had just asked Rosalie to sort some cards, something which was too difficult for her, so she lashed out because she couldn't do the task she had been set. This is not 'attention-seeking' behaviour, but is called in technical terms 'demand avoidance'. If Rosalie is taught a new sign for saying 'stop and go away', and as long as all the staff know that when she uses it they must act accordingly, she may not need to be aggressive in the future. At the moment the staff are not alert to Rosalie's attempts to signal when she wants to bring activities to an end: they don't all use Makaton (a signing system specifically for people with learning difficulties) or receive training in communication skills, so they also need to learn some new behaviours!

If you start from the point of view that a person's behaviour does have a function, you can try to avoid the stresses which lead to difficulties: to present activities which are right for them, and to provide enough and the right kind of support. It means that you don't just shrug your shoulders and keep out of the way of someone like Rosalie, or blame and punish her. Instead, you recognise that she isn't *choosing* not to learn or to behave badly: she just can't operate at this level of difficulty.

> **Key points**
>
> - Negative labels can create a vicious circle or self-fulfilling prophecy.
>
> - Accurate labels draw attention to 'differences' which may help you to explain or interpret someone's actions or behaviour.
>
> - Managing difficult behaviour relies on working out its *function*; in other words what it achieved for that person in that particular setting or situation.

2.4 Safeguards in behaviour programmes

Behaviour programmes should seek to build on a person's ways of controlling their environment. Punishment of any kind is not ethically acceptable in community care services even if it could be shown to work. Instead, behaviour programmes focus on building skills and helping people to develop alternatives which work for them. But planning in detail how to react to someone is a far cry from most everyday relationships, which is why we are considering it in this unit – it could even be seen as quite manipulative or controlling.

Should anyone consciously shape the behaviour of others by rewarding some behaviours and communication and not others? Are we all shaping people's behaviours anyway even if we haven't thought about it and it just happens in a haphazard way? Does it make a difference that we are dealing with people like Rosalie who have difficulty learning from the jumble of responses they usually come up against? Because we have moved beyond 'normal' social expectations we need a new set of rules.

Chad Botley, whom you heard on the audio cassette, stresses the need for staff to have a clear set of values and access to multidisciplinary input when dealing with difficult behaviour. He also identified the risk as that 'staff might tip over and respond physically instead of verbally in difficult or aggressive situations' and he also emphasised that structures should be available to 'provide a framework within which staff can feel safe to express their views and concerns'.

Activity 11 **Rules for managing difficult behaviour**

Allow about 15 minutes Imagine you are a member of staff who is being asked to respond to Rosalie in a particular way which has been set out in a written behaviour programme. See if you can come up with a list of rules that you would feel comfortable with, to guide you and your colleagues.

Comment My rules would include:

- The behaviour we are trying to 'treat' should be something which Rosalie could change, not something like fits which are always going to be out of her control.

- We should be helping her to manage things better for herself in future, not just taking something away from her.

- We should be aiming to help her do things she wants to do and opening up opportunities for her.

- We should find a way of working with her which keeps us and other residents safe.

- We shouldn't do anything against the law.

- We shouldn't damage her or hurt her. For example, I would not be willing to hit her, although I would hold her down to stop her hurting someone else if I had been shown how to do this properly.

- We shouldn't give her medication just to make life easier for us.

- We should have a properly qualified psychologist to help us work out what is best and then discuss the programme together so we all know how to put it into practice.

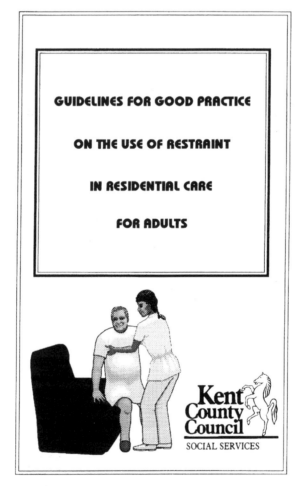

Staff need clear and agreed guidelines

Some agencies have developed codes of practice to formalise rules such as these. However, even where proper programmes are in place emergencies may arise. These often call for a quick response to cool someone down or to remove others from harm. Excessive force might easily be applied in such situations unless staff are given help in anticipating and dealing with emergencies. They may be frightened or at risk themselves. This is an area of practice which needs particular attention in guidelines and is often dealt with under the title of 'control and restraint' or 'physical interventions'. As a general principle 'reasonable' force in such situations involves the *minimum* needed to calm the person down. A model national policy (Harris *et al.*, 1996) advocates the notion of a 'gradient of control' whereby:

... when staff respond with [any] physical intervention, they follow a predetermined sequence which begins with the application of the least restrictive options and gradually increases the level of restriction. The sequence is terminated as soon as control is established over the person's behaviour.

(*Harris* et al., *1996, p. 35*)

Key points

- Behaviour programmes should aim to expand a person's skills and opportunities, not restrict them.

- People need safeguards if any sanctions are being applied to them by staff.

- Behaviour programmes are one area of practice which requires proper professional input and monitoring.

- Services should lay down codes of good practice in relation to challenging behaviour for all staff and detailed guidance in relation to individuals, especially if working with them safely might involve any physical intervention or restraint such as their being locked in or held down.

2.5 A service which broke the rules

Contrast the way Marie's unit and the psychologist dealt with Rosalie with the way Mr and Mrs D, who managed a residential home, treated people in their care. (Unlike the story about Marie and Rosalie, this is a real case which was considered at a public tribunal. The details are taken from evidence given at the hearing.) A young man called Darren had his glasses removed as a punishment. Another resident called Tom was hosed down outside whenever he had epileptic fits. These breaches of good practice eventually led to this home being closed under the Registered Homes Act and details of the regime there were spelt out in the tribunal's findings.

The chair of the tribunal challenged the owner about the way Tom had been treated suggesting that the owner had no 'understanding whatsoever of [his] vulnerability' and that 'it was wrong to deal with him in a punitive way'. The owner replied, 'It depends what you mean', and when asked 'Are you suggesting he was deliberately being difficult, acting out of spite?' she replied, 'They can be, yes'. This switch from 'he' in the question to 'they' in the answer suggests that the owner had made a blanket decision about people with learning difficulties rather than a careful assessment of Tom's particular abilities, needs or intentions. She put a gloss on her actions by using the notion that she was 'redirecting his activity', when clearly practices such as sending him outside in the cold for over an hour were designed to punish. The owners did not appear to understand that epileptic fits cannot be brought on at will: they just happen as a result of electric impulses in the brain. Not only were the punishments cruel but there was no point to them as Tom could not 'learn' to control his fits or to have them at a time when they were less inconvenient.

Abuse disclosures denied

Powys County Council is seeking to close a private home for adults with severe learning difficulties following allegations that residents were physically abused.

The owners of the home, Golfa View in Mid Wales, have denied the allegations and are appealing against de-registration at a registered homes tribunal next month.

A ten-month police investigation into the allegations has been dropped following advice from the Crown Prosecution Service that there was no case for further action.

Allegations of physical assault of residents and sexual harassment of staff at the home were made in anonymous phone calls to *Community Care* last week.

The allegations claimed:

- A young epileptic man was hosed down with cold water.
- An elderly incontinent woman received the same treatment.
- A boy who scratched himself had his hands tied behind his back.

(*Community Care*, 28 January 1993)

Nursing home boss jailed for abuse

Fat controller's horror home

This is where it is important to remind ourselves about the civil liberties of service users, as set out at the beginning of this unit. We began with a quote from Sobsey in which he said that do-gooders can overstep the mark to the extent that people with learning difficulties end up with less protection and fewer safeguards than convicted prisoners. An approach which begins with rights, the sort you considered in relation to Lynne in Unit 3, reminds everyone that it is *never* permissible to deprive people of ordinary things like watching television or food and drink as part of a 'programme'. Untrained staff may sometimes be asked to work within, or accept, set ways of responding to a particular individual without the information or training to check that it makes sense. They may be muddled by fancy language or specialist advice. For staff in such unenviable positions, it is useful to remember that if a professional of any kind gives advice about practice they should always be able to explain *why* they are recommending it and what benefit it will bring to the person concerned. Staff, however junior or untrained, have a duty to ask for such an explanation.

Before we move on, look back at the rules you set out for the staff implementing Rosalie's programme (Activity 11). Would your rules have prevented the things Mr and Mrs D did to Darren and Tom? If not, how might they be amended?

Key points

- There is no point in punishing someone for something they cannot change.

- Civil rights cannot be set aside just because someone displays challenging behaviour.

- The jargon of behaviour programmes can be misapplied to justify regimes where control is given higher priority than development and where individual well-being is being put at risk.

Section 3
Protection

Section 2 explored how far it is acceptable to 'control' or attempt to change someone's behaviour. In Rosalie's case you were looking at the need to intervene to stop her hurting other people. Now you will be considering a rather drastic intervention, tagging, which has been suggested as one way to protect a particular young man, Tony, from harming himself. Electronic tagging has sometimes been used in services for older people who 'wander' on the grounds that if they can be stopped from actually leaving their establishment, with all the risks that might entail, they can enjoy more freedom within the home and grounds. It has also been put forward as a way of monitoring people on bail. But it raises important civil liberties issues and is seen as a particularly intrusive form of surveillance. Many of the arguments we shall consider in relation to Tony might be applied in these other situations as well.

3.1 Assessing risk

Tony's case has been adapted from a situation reported in my local newspaper (a few details have been changed to protect his anonymity). Imagine Marie reading the paper when she gets home from work and zooming in on the issues because they echo challenges in her own work.

NORTHERN ECHO

by our very own correspondent

Tag our Tony, say parents

'Tag our son' plead the parents of autistic Tony Smith who are at the end of their tether trying to cope. They believe electronic tagging is the only way to stop their 23-year-old boy from vanishing in future and possibly even killing himself. In his second disappearing act within three months Tony spent two nights sleeping in below freezing temperatures before he was found.

'He can't help it, he's obsessed with lorries' his distraught mum said. 'He hears voices telling him to do things and one day he is going to come to harm just because someone tells him to do something daft. There's no way we can keep him under lock and key and I have other kids to look after ... it costs the police thousands to find him and bring him back.'

Tony has the mental age of a nine year old, and disappeared on Sunday with £5 in his pocket after going to get a paper. He was found cold and bedraggled on Thursday, 50 miles away, after a massive search operation.

Mr and Mrs Smith are due to meet police and social services chiefs today to discuss the tagging idea. 'The only alternative might be to lock him up and we don't want that,' said his dad.

Electronic tags are used by police to keep track of people on bail waiting for court appearances. Tony has done nothing wrong but could this be the right answer?

Activity 12   Protecting Tony's interests

Allow about 5 minutes   You will see that Tony's story is reported from his parents' point of view. Tony might not agree that this is the best solution to his difficulties.

Any decision of this gravity would have to be made in a formal meeting or case conference such as the one Mr and Mrs Smith are due to have with police and social services. Is there anyone else you would invite to that meeting and how could you ensure that Tony's interests were properly represented and protected in the discussion? Should Tony be there himself?

Comment   I think that it would be good for Tony to be there for at least part of the meeting. It would be good too if he had an advocate to work with him to bolster his confidence and ability to speak for himself, and if necessary to speak for him. I think I might also want an independent professional such as a psychologist there to make sure that everyone is working on the basis of accurate information.

Advocacy was introduced in Unit 10, in the context of volunteers or professional health or care workers acting as advocates for Jim and Marianne. Using Tony's story, you can explore the possible role of an advocate where a difficult decision involves weighing up rights and risks.

Activity 13   Pros and cons of tagging Tony

Allow about 10 minutes   Imagine you are at the case conference as Tony's advocate, with Tony's parents, social services and the police. You are there to put Tony's case in relation to the tagging idea. What arguments do you expect will be put for and against tagging? Jot down three pros and three cons.

Comment   **For**

- Tagging might stop Tony getting run over or lost.
- Tagging is better than locking Tony up.
- Tagging wouldn't be that noticeable, whereas calling out the police to find him might make people think he has done something wrong.

Against

- No one has asked Tony's opinion or assessed just how much risk he is in.
- Tony is 23. Despite his mental age, he should be treated as an adult unless there are very clear reasons not to, and that includes allowing him to come and go as he wishes.
- Tagging is a contravention of Tony's human rights.

A range of views are likely to be expressed during the meeting. For example, Tony's parents are clearly at the end of their tether and tagging might help to alleviate some of the strain of watching out for him all the time. The police are not too happy about the time and expense involved in bringing Tony back and the social services might also be glad if a way can be found to avoid emergencies like this in the future.

It is always a balancing act when you are considering restricting a person's freedom in order to stop them putting themselves at risk. It is one of those occasions when pragmatism seems to conflict with principle. On the face of it, the idea of tagging Tony looks harmless enough and could bring major benefits. But remember what Sobsey says: it conflicts with some very fundamental civil liberties. What justification can there be for limiting the freedom of a 23-year-old man in this way? And if Tony can be tagged, what is there to stop *any* parent asking the police to tag their wayward son?

What kind of assessment is necessary to inform this decision? Clearly the degree of risk involved has to be assessed, as does Tony's ability to understand his predicament and make his own decisions. Also, a range of possible options needs to be reviewed. The assessment process following this meeting is likely to focus on three questions:

How serious is the risk that Tony will leave home again and if he does what is the likelihood that he will come to harm while he is away? His parents have said that he hears voices and might do something dangerous if told to by someone else. Risk assessments may be phrased in terms of the *extent* of possible harm and the *likelihood* that it might happen. So you get different kinds of risk. There are situations which are 'minor accidents waiting to happen', like cutting your finger on the kitchen knife (which most of us do every now and then), and there are those where the damage would be devastating but is unlikely to occur, such as a nuclear accident. If the outcome of this assessment is that the risk to Tony is both life-threatening *and* very likely then action is certainly necessary.

What do we know about Tony and his capacity to make his own decisions and protect himself from harm? Tony has not done anything against the law and he cannot have his freedom removed, even for a good reason, unless he falls within the framework of the Mental Health Act 1983 which allows authorities such as health or social services or the police to intervene. After all, leaving home is a normal thing for a 23-year-old to do. But we would also want to look at Tony's situation in a more holistic way, at his relationships with his family, his current contact with services, his entitlement to benefits, his daily and weekly routine, and so on. These might be as important as Tony's 'ability' in assessing the situation and deciding what to do for the best.

What is the best intervention to address these concerns – that is, the solution which is least intrusive or stigmatising in the eyes of others? Tony's parents have seized on the idea of tagging as a magic solution in the way that ill people will seek out instant cures; but there may be other ways of protecting Tony which are not so extreme.

Another question which might be addressed in the meeting is 'why now?' because, as in many other situations, risk has been an ongoing feature in Tony's life. Sometimes when the anxiety gets too high someone will force the issue (as Tony's parents have by going to the local paper) but many vulnerable people face considerable risk and many parents and staff contain anxiety on a daily basis. Once the risk has been formally notified to management then action has to be taken to prevent it and protect the individual concerned. It is no wonder then, when services are so pressed, that they may shy away from explicit acknowledgement of risk in lots of circumstances. Once a decision has been made in the context of risk it will need to be monitored and reviewed regularly: this process is known as 'risk management'.

One of the problems inherent in this kind of situation is that there is no obviously right answer so people can be forgiven for hesitating to make any decision at all. But doing nothing may be the worst option, even if it is the path of least resistance. Do you think doing nothing is an option in Tony's situation?

Key points

- Sometimes restrictions *do* need to be applied to prevent someone from harming themselves.

- Advocacy specifically for the service user concerned can help to make sure their interests are paramount in any such decisions.

- Risk assessment should focus on the situation, the individual and the range of possible solutions, and anticipate risks rather than let things happen.

- When considering interventions which limit freedom formal safeguards should be used to guarantee civil liberties.

- Sometimes doing nothing is not a viable option.

3.2 About autism

One piece of information which needs to be considered in detail is that Tony has a label – he is autistic. This is not going to provide the key to the whole problem, but it is a place to start. Autism is a very specific form of learning disability/mental health problem. It may be that you work with people who have other specific difficulties, for example Downs syndrome or dementia. This section of the unit might guide you in seeking out information which helps you to be more aware of their needs.

Disability activists have argued very strongly against a 'medical model' of disability – one which looks for the roots of problems in an individual's impairment rather than in their social circumstances and the position of disabled people in society at large. When you look closer you can often see that problems which seemed to be 'caused' by a particular condition arise in the context of a wide range of factors including poverty, discrimination, isolation, lack of transport, inappropriate housing and lack of service provision. So problems experienced by Tony are not inevitably a direct consequence of autism. Nevertheless, it is worth understanding what is meant by this label to get a clear picture of how it affects him and the decisions he can make for himself.

Autism

Autism is a permanent condition arising in childhood, leading to a range of impairments of varying severity. These include difficulties in:

- social interaction

- social communication

- imagination.

It is also characterised by repetitive or obsessive behaviour 'as shown by stereotyped play patterns, abnormal preoccupations or resistance to change.' (Harris *et al.*, 1996, p. 6).

Usually these are associated with learning difficulties. But some people with autism are of average or above average intelligence, although they experience similar difficulties in relating to other people. This is called Asperger's syndrome.

According to a booklet published by the Autistic Society, because autism affects the way people make contact with others, a child or adult may appear 'aloof or indifferent' and talk *at* rather than *with* others. They may not understand or pick up on facial expressions, gestures or tone of voice. They may understand and use language very literally, not in a social way. Some autistic people have peculiar abilities alongside these impairments (for example in music, drawing or arithmetic like the character played by Dustin Hoffman in the film *Rainman*).

The condition was first identified in 1943 by an American psychiatrist called Kanner and is a very complex disorder which is still being unravelled. Many authorities believe the difficulties are caused by an underlying neurological mechanism. While most children learn relatively easily and spontaneously, autistic children have to have things really spelt out and signposted for them. They need to be taught in a very structured way and have the *consequences* of what they do very specifically pointed out to them. It has been suggested that just as dyslexia is sometimes a form of 'word blindness' or 'number blindness', autism is a form of 'mind blindness'. Baron-Cohen, a researcher who has taught autistic children, says they:

> ... appeared singularly oblivious to what others were **thinking** – it did not seem to occur to them that others might think them odd, or funny or that others might **think** anything at all. The other thing that struck me was that their behaviour and speech seemed to be largely lacking in any **self-reflection**.

(Baron-Cohen, 1992, p. 9)

Dustin Hoffman in 'Rainman'

Activity 14   **Does autism make a difference?**

Allow about 5 minutes   You remember that we were looking at this information to help us decide if there were extenuating circumstances which might influence the decision that would be taken at Tony's case conference. Quickly reread the box on autism and jot down any points you think you would want to explore in the context of the risks Tony faces.

Comment   I noted, for example, that Tony might be unaware that a stranger offering him a lift might have malicious intentions. I also wondered about his road safety skills and whether these could be improved by the kind of structured teaching described above. But I was left wondering about how much he understood of the risks he faced and/or how he could learn to keep himself safe ... the information about autism in general could not answer these points with particular reference to Tony.

Understanding a condition such as autism can help us avoid situations where parents or individuals are blamed for unusual behaviour patterns. This returns us to the issue of labelling. Uta Frith, an expert on autism, challenges the notion that a label is necessarily negative. It may lead to people being treated with more understanding.

> *To me it is a very false idea of kindness not to acknowledge that someone, through no fault but nature's, suffers from a biological disorder. Surely, to recognise that some people have a disorder means to recognise that they have a right to an allowance being made for their handicap? This is at least a first step towards a kinder treatment.*
>
> (Frith, 1992, p. 19)

Key points

- Sometimes you need to find out details about a particular condition or impairment so that you can plan an appropriate level of support or intervention.

- Autism is thought to be caused by an underlying neurological mechanism which leads to specific learning disabilities and problems in making sense of the environment: these may co-exist with islands of brilliance.

- Structured routines and teaching opportunities can help children and adults with autism to learn a wide range of skills.

- Autism as a 'condition' should be taken into account in assessing the risks faced by someone like Tony, but on a very individual basis and within the context of a more holistic assessment.

3.3 Capacity

We have seen that Tony decides to leave home every now and then. If any intervention is to be set in motion to stop him, a crucial factor in the assessment and decision making is to examine whether he has 'capacity'. This is a legal term which is shorthand for his ability to understand risk and make decisions for himself. This assessment will be made primarily by a psychologist and there are two ways in which it may be made (Murphy and Clare, 1995).

- First, it might be made on the basis of an existing *diagnosis* which identifies an individual as one of a group who are considered to have a shared lack of capacity. For example, *all* people with severe learning disabilities are deemed not to be able to consent to sexual acts under the terms of the 1956 Sexual Offences Act. This is also called a 'status' test (Law Commission, 1995, p. 32, para. 3.2).

- Alternatively, a more individual and specific *functional* approach could be taken. This involves assessment of the particular skills or knowledge needed in relation to a specific issue. As the Law Commission puts it: whether the individual is able 'at the time when a particular decision has to be made, to understand its nature and effects' (1995, p. 33, para. 3.5).

Activity 15   **A functional assessment**

Allow about 10 minutes   How would you go about conducting a functional assessment of whether Tony has 'capacity' in relation to his decision to leave home for brief periods of time? (Assume you can consult with those professionals currently working with him.) I've suggested a *functional* assessment at this stage because I'd feel very uncomfortable about arguing for a blanket decision saying that *all* people with learning difficulties, or *all* autistic people, are a risk to themselves when they go out and should be tagged. I want this assessment to be very much geared to Tony and his individual abilities and situation.

Write a list of five areas you would want to explore in your assessment.

Comment   My list would include:

- his safety crossing roads

- his sense of direction and local knowledge

- his ability to use public transport

- his behaviour towards others

- his ability to perceive risk in the behaviour of others towards him.

Often such decisions are made informally within services in the context of staff meetings or individual planning meetings. A more formal way is to officially recognise a person's lack of 'capacity' and need for help. For example, their affairs could be administered through the civil court if they are acknowledged to be unable to manage their own finances. In extreme cases they might come within the terms of the 1983 Mental Health Act because they have a mental disorder, in which case they can be taken into hospital for assessment or treatment. Decisions under the Act are made by one or two doctors (usually psychiatrists) with input from an Approved Social Worker who has had additional training in mental health. Most people with learning difficulties do not fall within the stricter definition of mental impairment which could lead to them being detained or 'sectioned', but Tony might be an exception.

In practice, the kinds of interventions required by Richard, Rosalie and Tony are likely to be set in motion by an informal group of workers and managers who think they have the best interests of their clients at heart rather than by a formal/legal assessment process. What you have been looking at are some of the frameworks you can use to check this out.

Key points

- 'Capacity' is a legal term. Where it is judged that someone is not able to manage their affairs on account of mental impairment or incapacity, the courts can make special provision for that person.

- 'Functional capacity' is the term for a person's ability to take a particular decision for themselves.

- Lack of capacity may be formally acknowledged under the Mental Health Act 1983 and other civil legislation.

- Often services make professional judgments about capacity as it affects people in everyday matters. This has the benefit of being informal but it may mean that people are not able to challenge the service's decisions.

3.4 The least intrusive intervention

We began to examine the underlying principles in Tony's case by separating out three basic issues. You have looked at assessment of risk and assessment of Tony's ability to take decisions on his own behalf. Now you are going to consider the last question, the intervention being proposed – tagging – to see if it conforms to principles enshrined in both the Children Act 1989 and the Mental Health Act 1983, and also in proposed (but at the time of writing unenacted) legislation about protecting vulnerable adults. The key question is whether this is the 'least restrictive' or the 'least intrusive' procedure. Professional ethics might also raise questions about stigmatising Tony. However, the most important issue is whether the same degree of safety could be provided by a lower-level, more ordinary kind of measure. Any deliberation should put the proposed intervention on trial rather than putting Tony under the spotlight.

Activity 16   **Is tagging the right intervention?**

Allow about 5 minutes   Now do a quick review of whether you think tagging is an appropriate strategy. Is it the 'least restrictive alternative' or can you think of better ways of keeping Tony safe?

Comment   What have you decided? I thought about alternatives such as:

- a teaching programme to help him find his way around

- work on road safety or public transport training

- providing him with a phone card to make it easier for him to ring home

- pointing out to him places he could go for help if he got lost, such as the bus depot or the police station.

I did not rule tagging out completely but came round to the idea that there were less drastic measures to try first.

I also thought that respite care might be appropriate. Tony's behaviour was not only due to autism. The request for tagging was *tied* to his parents' anxiety and could be read as a signal of their 'overload'.

Landmark places

Even though this case might have to lead to a formal intervention, there are many circumstances in which the same principles need to be applied more informally to risk assessment and individual care planning. It is important to ensure that protection is not used as a rationale for unnecessarily restricting someone's opportunities or infringing their civil liberties.

Key points

- Interventions should be the least intrusive and stigmatising possible.

- Under the Mental Health Act 1983 people are entitled to the 'least restrictive' treatments and living arrangements.

- More ordinary alternatives can often be found if situations are assessed in detail and creative support made available.

Section 4

Regimes

You have now worked in detail through two cases where the risks associated with an individual's behaviour had to be managed either, as in Rosalie's case, to protect others from harm, or, as in Tony's, to ensure his own safety. Where such decisions are not subject to the kind of detailed and personalised scrutiny we have worked through they can mistakenly be allowed to justify a whole regime in which restrictive practices and restraints go unquestioned.

4.1 Why do residential homes fail their clients?

One place where issues of control and protection went wrong over a very long period was the children's home which became the focus of the 'Pin-down' scandal. In this home issues of control came to dominate the regime and a policy of 'grounding' and 'time out' was used without any proper safeguards or external monitoring. Eventually this led to an extensive independent inquiry which documented the regime and its management in detail.

Activity 17

Allow about 30 minutes

Towards an understanding of the corruption of care

Read Chapter 24 in the Reader by Wardhaugh and Wilding. The authors draw out eight factors which they felt had played a part in creating and sustaining this pattern of control and repression. You will see that the authors use some frameworks you have already read about, such as Goffman's analysis of institutions. (You may recognise some of his ideas resurfacing in this analysis.) As you read, make a list of the eight 'propositions' with a one or two line explanation to help you remember the main ideas under each heading.

Comment

My notes looked like this:

1   Neutralisation of normal moral concerns – depersonalise residents have to 'obey', stop feeling pity for others' suffering – used Pin-down to break their will.

2   Power and powerlessness – staff feel powerless and have little influence over the way the place is run but they have power over the residents.

3   Particular groups at risk – people who are not valued or are stereotyped are most at risk when managers just want to 'keep the lid on' the place.

4   Managers do not set clear aims nor do outside people like professionals or lay people.

5   Enclosed, inward-looking places.

6   Staff unsupervised and no formal accountability.

7   People do not feel they can challenge professionals or those above them in the hierarchy.

8   Some client groups are seen as less than human, adults seen as children, and so on.

Do you agree with my feeling that there were some overlaps with Goffman's account of total institutions?

The Staffordshire pin-down scandal

Date	Event
October 1989	A solicitor obtains a High Court injunction to stop the use of pin-down in a number of homes, allegedly practised since 1983
March–April 1990	A routine SSI inspection of child protection services in the county did not consider any allegations; its conclusions that the SSD failed to follow agreed procedures are not published until October
June 1990	A World in Action programme alleges that 100 young people have been subject to pin-down; the council says it will commission an independent review of the 'discontinued' use of pin-down
July–August 1990	Meanwhile, the SSI investigates four homes at the request of the Secretary of State; it reports in September
August 1990	The independent inquiry into pin-down begins, under Barbara Kahan and Allan Levy; Levy refers the Fundwell allegations to the district auditor
September 1990	Two SSI reports criticising management and staff in four homes are discussed by the council; SSD director Barry O'Neill proposed a special child care project team
October 1990	The Levy inquiry widens its scope to take in allegations that a convicted paedophile took children on outings from one or more homes, including those where pin-down was allegedly practised; a police report on various allegations goes to the Crown Prosecution Service, which later decides to take no action
December 1990	SSD director Barry O'Neill takes early retirement due to ill health; the Levy inquiry, after sitting for 75 days and hearing 153 witnesses, is not able to report until May but the council refuses to indemnify it against possible legal action
May 1991	Christine Walby becomes new SSD director, from Solihull; an SSI inspector, David Bartle, acts as a child care consultant to the authority on a three-year contract
30 May	The full report is launched; Levy, Kahan and the council hold press conferences; at least 50 young people are said to be seeking damages from the council

(*Community Care*, 24 June 1991)

'Care' regime that relied on humiliation

Inquiry condemns pin-down method of isolation and confrontation as wholly negative and entirely unacceptable.

'Another week of solitary confinement for X has had some rather peculiar effects. He is talking to himself a great deal and we have had tears several times during the course of the week. Sleeping in staff report incidents of him talking in his sleep.'

Thus the log book of a children's home in Stoke-on-Trent records matter-of-factly the appalling reality of a regime which for almost six years cast a shadow over the lives of hundreds of youngsters in residential care in Staffordshire. The regime was called 'pin-down'.

An independent inquiry report on the affair published yesterday pulls no punches. The regime was, it says, fundamentally dependent on isolation, humiliation and confrontation. It was wholly negative and entirely unacceptable.

(*Guardian*, 31 May 1991)

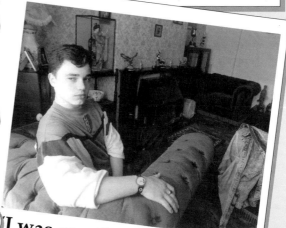

'I was crawling up the wall. I couldn't cope'

Fear of silence haunts 16-year-old kept in solitary confinement.

'There were two rooms specifically for pin-down, two rooms on one corridor. There was one where they had a big window that faced the road so you could see everybody going past. But the one I was in just faced an old couple's flat, the kitchen.'

(*Guardian*, 31 May 1991)

The Staffordshire Pin-down scandal

Solidarity and not isolation ...

Condensing these suggestions even further I came up with four key issues which might signal a service which is not providing the kind of safeguards I talked about at the beginning of the unit. These are:

1   difficult clients who are not valued and whose human status is not recognised

2   direct care staff who cannot influence, challenge or complain

3   managers who do not provide supervision or take responsibility

4   a home which is isolated from the outside world and professional debates.

Clearly there are problems at each of these levels. If they are arranged in reverse order they bring to mind a waterfall in that each level blames and dumps the responsibility on to the level below. Read them in reverse and you will see what I mean.

- isolated from outside world and professional debates

- managers do not provide supervision or take responsibility

- direct care staff cannot influence, challenge or complain

- difficult clients who are not valued and whose human status is not recognised.

4.2 System abuse

The paper you have just read opens out our discussion of abuse. We began with a focus on the interpersonal – on things going bad between a carer and the person they are caring for. Now we have moved on to broader social issues – to inequality which leads to some people being *de*valued, and to systems which lead to low paid work and poor management. Decisions taken at a distance from the immediate environment can also have a devastating effect on individuals and their experience of receiving care.

Richard, the young man for whom Marie was keyworker, for example, had a 'history' of being moved from one placement to another. After several foster placements he ended up in a residential school many miles from his home town. This had the effect of loosening his ties with his family. His mother was poor and found it difficult to travel with her other children to visit him. Gradually they lost touch. And as we have seen he was placed in a large residential unit which did not have many black staff or any support for his cultural identity.

Gil (1982) calls this kind of abuse 'system abuse' because it happens as a result of actions and decisions which are structural and beyond the remit of a single individual. So we need to look beyond the behaviour of individual staff, or of a single establishment, to the values and organisation of the wider system. Within children's services, Gil defines this kind of abuse as:

> ... any system, programme, policy, procedure or individual interaction with a child [or adult] in placement that abuses, neglects, or is detrimental to the child's health, safety, or emotional and physical well-being, or in any way exploits or violates the child's basic rights.
>
> (cited in Westcott, 1991, p. 9)

Within the generic term 'institutional abuse' Gil discriminates abuses happening at different levels:

> • 'programme abuse' occurs when programmes within an institution are abusive or neglectful, like the Pin-down example
>
> • 'system abuse' is ... not perpetrated by any single person or programme, but by the immense and complicated child care system, stretched beyond its limits and incapable of guaranteeing safety to all children in care ...   (p. 11)

How a blind eye was turned to kicks, punches and torments

Three convicted after reign of terror at care home

Ashworth patient may have died from drug dosage, inquiry told

Patient 'beaten every day'

Elderly 'suffer in private homes'

Key points

- Abuse may arise not only because of individual carers or settings but because of wider societal problems and inequalities: this is sometimes called 'system abuse'.

- Institutional abuse can happen at the level of the 'programme' or of the wider 'system'.

- Abuse can come about because of a failure to provide adequate or appropriate support as well as through punitive, restrictive or stigmatising forms of care.

Conclusion

In this unit you have looked at areas of care which cross normal social boundaries and at how this leaves individuals to manage painful dilemmas within settings which sometimes mirror society's devaluation of people needing care and those who work with them. We have considered how difficult it is to maintain professional boundaries when performing intimate tasks and we have seen how staff can become restrictive or punitive in the face of risk or difficult behaviour. We have also seen that openly debating these issues can help to take the sting out of them and that agreed and negotiated guidelines can help staff to face difficult situations and provide safeguards for service users.

Now let's look again at the core questions for this unit together with some key points relating to each.

How can boundaries be respected in situations where intimate care is being given?

- Caring relationships often cross the boundaries set by 'normal social rules' and once these have been breached it is hard to know where the new lines should be set.

- Intimate care involves 'dirty work' which, because it is a taboo subject, is often shrouded in silence and not acknowledged within the official structures and documents of an organisation; it is also often left to women.

- Intimate care stirs up difficult feelings which are usually censored but still affect the way people care for each other and the unofficial culture of the establishment.

How can choices, rights and autonomy be balanced against the need to protect people in receipt of care who put themselves at risk of harm?

- Often the philosophy of services is muddled about when they will treat people on the basis of 'normality' and when on the basis of 'special need'.

- People should be allowed to make their own mistakes unless they lack 'capacity' to make a particular decision for themselves or are at significant risk.

In what situations and with what safeguards are people entitled to use physical power to control or restrain someone to stop them harming themselves or another person?

- Control sometimes has to be part of the caring relationship but only if safeguards are in place to ensure that any intervention is in someone's best interests or will prevent him or her from harming others.

- There are legal principles to consult when making decisions on when and how to control someone's behaviour.

When and how can systems become abusive?

- Sometimes establishments become distorted or controlling, especially if there is a lack of guidance, training and support for staff, or inadequate resources to support informal carers.

- Pressures within care relationships and settings often reflect wider social problems such as the isolation or poverty of people who rely on services, and wider inequalities on the basis of race, gender or class.

Study skills: The summer break

Just to remind you, there is a six-week gap between TMA 05 and TMA 06. That means you can spread the four units of Block 6 over six weeks. This is to give you some space to take a summer break if you want to. But obviously you don't want to lose your momentum too much. You will need to keep an eye on your progress through the block. Anyway, we hope you will feel refreshed after this brief slackening of the pace.

References

Baron-Cohen, S. (1992) 'The theory of mind hypothesis of autism: history and prospects of the idea', *The Psychologist*, Vol. 5, pp. 9–12.

Brown, H. and Smith, H. (1989) 'Whose "ordinary life" is it anyway?', *Disability, Handicap and Society*, Vol. 4, No. 2, pp. 105–19.

Craft, A. and Brown, H. (1994) 'Personal relationships and sexuality: the staff role', in Craft, A. (ed.) *Practice Issues in Sexuality and Learning Disabilities*, Routledge, London, pp. 10–22.

Emerson, E., Barratt, S., Bell, C., Cummings, R., Hughs, H., McCool, C., Toogood, A. and Mansell, J. (1987) *The Special Development Team: Developing Services for People with Severe Learning Disabilities and Challenging Behaviours*, Centre for the Applied Psychology of Social Care, University of Kent at Canterbury.

Enfield Social Services (1996) *Guidelines on Professional Boundaries*, London Borough of Enfield, London.

Frith, U. (1992) 'Cognitive development and cognitive deficit', *The Psychologist*, Vol. 5, pp. 13–19.

Gil, E. (1982) 'Institutional abuse of children in out-of-home care', in Hanson, R. (ed.) *Institutional Abuse of Children and Youth*, The Haworth Press, N. Yorkshire.

Harris, J., Allen, D., Cornick, M., Jefferson, A. and Mills, R. (1996) *Physical Interventions: A Policy Framework*, BILD, Kidderminster.

Hochschild, A. (1983) *The Managed Heart*, University of California Press, Berkeley.

Hughes, E. (1971) 'Good people and dirty work', in *The Sociological Eye: Selected Papers*, Aldine Atherton, Chicago.

Law Commission (1995) *Mental Incapacity Law*, Cm 231, HMSO, London.

Lawler, J. (1991) *Behind the Screens: Nursing Somology and the Problem of the Body*, Churchill Livingstone, Melbourne.

Lowe, K. and Felce, D. (1995) 'The definition of challenging behaviour in practice', *British Journal of Learning Disabilities*, Vol. 23, pp. 118–23.

Menzies, I. (1970) *The Functioning of Social Systems as a Defence Against Anxiety*, Tavistock, London.

Murphy, G.H. and Clare, I.C.H. (1995) 'Adults' capacity to make decisions affecting the person: psychologists' contribution', in Bull, R. and Carson, D. (eds) *Handbook of Psychology in Legal Contexts*, J. Wiley & Sons, Chichester, pp. 97–128.

Oliver, J. (1983) 'The caring wife', in Finch, J. and Groves, D. (eds) *A Labour of Love: Women, Work and Caring*, Routledge & Kegan Paul, London, pp. 72–89.

Pascall, G. (1986) *Social Policy: A Feminist Analysis*, Tavistock, London.

Sinason, V. (1992) *Mental Handicap and the Human Condition*, Free Association Books, London.

Sobsey, D. (1994) *Violence and Abuse in the Lives of People with Disabilities*, Brookes, Baltimore.

Thompson, D., Clare, I. and Brown, H. (1997) 'Not such an "ordinary" relationship: the role of women support staff in relation to men with learning disabilities who have difficult sexual behaviour', *Disability and Society*, Vol. 12, No. 4, pp. 573–92.

Westcott, H. (1991) *Institutional Abuse of Children: From Research to Policy*, NSPCC, London.

Acknowledgements

I should like to thank Peter McGill of the Tizard Centre for contributing to the section on autism.

Grateful acknowledgement is made to the following sources for permission to use material in this unit:

Text

'Abuse disclosures denied', *Community Care*, 28th January 1993. Published by permission of the editor of *Community Care*; Richmond, T. (1997) 'Tag our Tony, say parents', *Milton Keynes Citizen*. Adapted by permission; Marchant, C. (1991) 'Challenging conduct', *Community Care*, 24th June 1991. Published by permission of the editor of *Community Care*; Brindle, D. (1991) ' "Care" regime that relied on humiliation', *Guardian*, 31st May 1991. © Guardian Newspapers Ltd 1991;

Illustrations

Pp. 8, 12, 16 (bottom), 19, 49: Brenda Prince/Format; pp. 9, 16 (top): Sally and Richard Greenhill; p. 34: Courtesy of Kent County Council Social Services; p. 42: The Ronald Grant Archive; p. 48: News Team International/photo: Joel Chant.

Unit 23
Drawing the Line

Prepared for the course team by Hilary Brown

While you are working on Unit 23, you will need:
- Course Reader
- Offprints Book
- Audio Cassette 6, parts 3 and 4
- Media Notes
- Wallchart

Contents

Introduction

You have seen throughout this course that caring is not just an ordinary relationship where common sense is a good enough guide. For example, Unit 3 discussed the need for home care assistants to establish boundaries in their relationships and Units 8 and 9 looked at the importance of care planning. In Unit 22 you explored some particularly difficult areas, including:

- intimate care, control and protection as areas which present particular challenges for those who care and those who are 'cared for'

- the dynamics of residential care and how these could go wrong

- why workers and family carers might find intimate care issues threatening because they move an otherwise 'social' relationship into uncharted waters

- the risks to civil liberties and integrity which people being cared for face in their daily interactions

- the idea of agreed guidance as one way of bringing difficult issues out into the open and strengthening professional boundaries where confusion about roles could slip over into abuse.

This unit explores these issues further. It is designed to help you draw the line between the occasional (some might say inevitable) 'ups and downs' of ordinary relationships and those real abuses of power which have to be challenged in the interests of both children and adults. In Unit 22 we reviewed the issues from inside the caring relationship. In this unit the focus is on making those judgments in more ordinary settings, in families and communities. We explore when, and in what circumstances, public 'authorities' intervene by crossing the thresholds of people's private lives.

This time you are on the outside looking in, because one important function of social and health care professionals is to step in when ordinary, unregulated, private relationships break down or go too far. So although there are some echoes of the issues you looked at in the last unit, in this one we come at them from a different angle.

You will be looking at what is meant by the term 'abuse', how decisions are made in situations where abuse is alleged or suspected, and at what point intervention should be initiated. The unit covers abuse as it affects both children and adults and deals with different forms of abuse and abusing. The material is not meant to be either voyeuristic or uncomfortable for the sake of it. It is designed to help you face up to abuse in the lives of people who use caring services and in your own life, and to search out the options and make changes. The core questions are listed overleaf.

Core questions

- How is 'abuse' defined?

- What are the different legal and professional contexts for child and adult protection?

- What criteria can be used for judging the seriousness of different kinds of abuse and abusing?

- Why does abuse happen and what pressures can lead to abusive behaviour?

- What part do gender, race, age and poverty play in the dynamics of abusive relationships?

Section 1
A health warning

The issues we shall be considering are distressing and shocking. It is a natural response to want to distance ourselves from them by thinking 'this couldn't happen in my family or my service or my neighbourhood'. But of course abuse does happen to ordinary people, in ordinary homes, day centres and schools. That is why everyone needs to think through the issues, to be prepared and to be well informed.

There are several reasons why you might find this subject particularly disturbing and it is worthwhile thinking about these to help you put support in place before you start, particularly if you anticipate the unit touching on painful memories or issues in your current situation.

1.1   You may have missed the signs

You may know individuals who, with the wisdom of hindsight, you now realise were being abused. You may regret that you did not recognise their distress or respond to things they were trying to tell you. Twenty years ago I worked with a young woman who had been admitted to a group home after living alone with her father in a remote country village. Her mother had died many years before and she had not had contact with services. Her father had rejected any help he had been offered and until recently, when he had been incapacitated by a stroke, he preferred to 'keep Diane busy at home'. She was very difficult and withdrawn and had quite significant learning disabilities which made it easier to wrap up her distress and aggression as something to do with her condition rather than with what had happened to her. The fashionable term in use at that time was that she was 'non-compliant'; nowadays she would have been labelled as having 'challenging behaviour'. She also had a vaginal infection which the GP said was the worst she had ever seen. We all found her difficult: she wouldn't wash or look after herself, she was frustrating in that she wouldn't join in activities or pull her weight in the house. Looking back, all the signs and signals point to the fact that she had been sexually abused prior to moving to the group home but at the time it did not cross anyone's mind.

It is hard to judge practice in the past by today's standards: new awarenesses allow us to see things in a different light. It is important to acknowledge that we all make mistakes, and rather than cover them over by denial or by trivialising them, to see them as opportunities to learn for the future.

1.2   You may have been abusive yourself

Another reason for looking back with regret is if you have witnessed bad practice which you either did not recognise as such, or did not feel strong enough to challenge. In the next unit you will be listening to an experienced worker who was drawn into a culture of violence in a children's home and who describes the difficulties he experienced in knowing what to do about it. Worse still, you might have done something which you now consider to have been abusive. It may be that you feel you have sometimes reached the end of your tether, perhaps at work with a client, or at home with a partner, or with your children. It is important to keep incidents in proportion but also to challenge patterns in which violence, whether verbal or physical, becomes a way of resolving issues or releasing tension.

1.3 You may have been abused

Studying this unit may bring back memories for you, or bring things to the surface which you have tried to keep buried. You may remember incidents which you have pushed to the back of your mind.

At a recent training day David Lewis suddenly found himself remembering that he had been sexually molested when he was about 13. He had been going home from swimming around the back of the park and an older boy had pushed him into the railings and made him have oral sex. David hadn't wanted to show anyone how afraid he had been: he didn't tell anyone at the time and he hadn't told anyone since. But learning about sexual abuse for his job as a manager of a day centre had brought it all back. The sudden onset of this buried memory made David quite anxious as he lives in a small community and he wouldn't want anyone to tell his wife.

Nearly three out of five women aged 16–21 and over a quarter of men in the same age group have experienced unwanted sexual attention according to a recent survey (Kelly *et al.*, 1991), and 4 per cent of young women and 2 per cent of young men have been more seriously sexually abused, so David is not alone in having to face these memories.

1.4 You may be in an abusive relationship now

Abuse may not necessarily be in the past. You may find this unit especially difficult if you are currently being abused in a relationship at home or at work. The examples and exercises may make you question whether you can or should be standing up for yourself more. You may have accepted violence or intimidation as inevitable, but come to see them as an infringement of your rights and dignity. You may need to get support or information from beyond your usual social network to help you leave a violent relationship, find an alternative service, or move on from a job which puts you at risk or is making you feel unhappy or unsafe. You may not want things to continue the way they are but you may be afraid to challenge them, or feel that you have no options.

Estimates vary about the prevalence of domestic violence but it is thought to occur in between 10 and 30 per cent of heterosexual relationships (Holder *et al.*, 1994) and in a half of cases in which a woman is being abused at least one child is being abused also. Men can also be on the receiving end of such abuse although this does not happen as frequently. Thinking through the issues in this unit may help you to clarify what you have a right to in your own relationships and your options for getting support and keeping safe.

Activity 1   Caring for yourself

Take as long as you need   Think carefully if there are any reasons why this unit might be particularly painful or challenging for you. Jot down on a piece of paper any times when:

(a)   you have felt abused by someone yourself

(b)   you have been concerned about someone else's behaviour

(c)   you have felt afterwards that your own relationships or practice have verged on being bullying or abusive.

Is there someone you can talk to about these times?

Are there lessons you have learnt?

Do you think you need help to keep you safe or to help you think clearly about the issues as they come up at home, in your work or in the context of your caring relationships and responsibilities?

Comment   You might want to talk to your tutor, to a counsellor or to a helpline or service which specialises in responding to people who are troubled about different kinds of abuse.

Key points

- Stepping in to prevent abuse is an important function of social and health care professionals.

- Considering abuse can trigger painful memories or feelings.

- If the material in this unit is likely to be painful for you, think now about where you can look for support.

Section 2
Different forms of abuse

To begin the unit I return to our fictionalised case study. In Unit 22 you met Marie who had just embarked on her career as a carer. Her next-door neighbour is Pat, an ordinary member of the public. As in Marie's story, a number of themes and threads have been woven together from real life. Even if they seem a bit fantastical, Pat's problems are those faced by many people at some time in their lives, although perhaps not all on one day!

Pat

Pat is Marie's next-door neighbour. She has had a rough week and has gone to visit her sister-in-law Bernice for a break. She explains over a cup of coffee how it all started and how it made her think.

'Well ... it was wet last Thursday and I hate November: the wind was really cold and I hate how it gets dark even though it is only 4 pm. I left work in a real hurry because I just had to get the shopping in. You know what it's like when you are out of cereal and there is no bread for anyone's sandwiches in the morning. I left the papers I was sorting for old Mitchell in a terrible mess and I still couldn't find the letter from Bates Limited that he kept asking for all morning. He had a real go at me about it and shouted at me right there in the front office with all the other girls listening in. If only I could have unearthed it before I left I could have relaxed and left work behind me for the evening. The more I think about it now I am sure that I gave it to him anyway. Last time he got really mad about something he had taken it out of my file himself and two weeks later he came and just dropped it in my in-tray without any word of explanation or apology. Perhaps I could find another job, although there isn't much around at the moment and the new mortgage we have just taken out makes it very difficult. We can't afford to take any risks ... well you can't these days can you? I still don't know where I could have filed Bates's letter ...

'When I got to the supermarket they were out of sandwich spread. It's always the way ... when things go wrong at work they usually go wrong at home as well. I knew Jesse would be cross and refuse to take anything proper to school ... if he can't have sandwich spread he won't have anything except a bag of crisps. I got in a right state wondering if I had time to go to the corner shop on my way home but you never know if they will have any there. If Superight don't have it probably the corner shop won't have it either so I knew he would just have to stew in his own juice. Then there I was at the checkout and what a queue! Jason Jones was on the till and although he's a nice lad he really isn't very quick, I don't know why they hired him. The woman in front ... she had a really nice emerald green jacket ... well she was taking ages unloading her trolley with the 'help' of her toddler. Well, I saw it coming really. Of course, the little girl wanted a chocolate egg: they were all wrapped up in shiny paper with little Father Christmases on top with darling little white fluffy beards. It was all so predictable looking back on it. 'Want one,' she said, but Mum says 'no'. 'Want one,' she said again. Mum said 'no' again, this time a bit louder. I just started to say 'I know how you feel, I've been there myself when mine were younger,' and I could tell the woman was getting tired and frazzled. And then suddenly, before I could get my mouth open, sort of out of nowhere, Mum lifted her out of the trolley and slapped her on the side of her thigh so hard the noise seemed to echo around the whole store. The little girl didn't scream, she just seemed to slump into the trolley seat in this sudden awful hush as everyone looked round. And I thought she seemed so shocked and small.

'I couldn't bear it ... I thought "Oh God! Did I ever do that? Surely I wouldn't have ever hit mine so hard". I didn't know if I should say something ... for an awful moment I thought she was going to do it again because all of a sudden the little girl let out a scream of rage and pain and her Mum was shouting at her, telling her to shut up and threatening to hit her again 'properly' when she got home. Somehow she got her bill paid and her shopping loaded up and they went off into the dark evening. Well, it really upset me. Should I have said anything? Or done anything? Should I have called social services? Oh of course not, it happens all the time ... she was just having a hard time. Do you mind if I have another chocolate biscuit? Young single mum I expect and it wouldn't help to be spying on her or reporting her to the authorities ... she's probably doing her best and anyway the little girl was whinging. If it had been me with my kids on a bad day I might have done the same ... But all the way home I kept thinking of the little girl's shocked expression, and I kept thinking, "is she tucked up in bed with it all forgotten and forgiven now or is she being hit again, and what if I read tomorrow in the paper that a child has been found dead?"

'I know I was getting it all out of proportion and after all who am I to preach, because just as I left the checkout myself I suddenly remembered I'd forgotten to drop mother's prescription in at the chemist's. If I concentrated on my own responsibilities instead of criticising everyone else I might get on better. So I decided to drop it off at Boots and then call in on my way home and give it to her ... if she runs out of pills she gets such bad heartburn and I didn't want that on my conscience. I did have a lucky break because I found a parking space and there was no queue. So, five minutes later, with the pills in my pocket I screeched up outside the flat. The lights were on but they seemed to take ages to come to the door.

'Dad was grumbling as soon as he opened the door. "Alright, alright, alright, Pat, I've only got one pair of bloody hands. She's gone and done it again ... wet herself ... just as I was getting dinner. I told her if she keeps doing it she'll have to go into a home ... it's no good, she does it just to get at me and I've had it up to here." I tried to apologise to Dad and calm him down a bit. "I just popped round to drop off her pills. You sound like you've had a bad day but you mustn't blame her, it isn't her fault." "It's alright for you, you don't have to wash the sheets or get up when she does it in the night ... it's just for attention, she does it just to get me going." "I'm sure she doesn't really, Dad. I'll take the sheets if you like. How has her stomach been?" "Ask her your bloody self," he said angrily. Well I did and she wouldn't say but I could see she had been uncomfortable all day. I keep trying not to notice things are getting impossible, but Dad can't really manage much longer on his own, and I don't know if a home is the answer. It'll cost a mint, they will end up selling the flat and although I know it's not right to even think about it, we had been counting on getting some of the capital from that flat for the kids. Oh I feel ashamed even talking about it, but Jesse wants to go to college so much and it's the only way we could afford to help him, but if it all goes on residential care we'll have to think again.

'And then Dad was going on about my aunt. "Your Aunty Gill was round again yesterday ... says her Derek has gone and got himself a girlfriend in that home for mongols he lives in and that they are thinking of getting engaged ... well I ask you, I haven't got much time for all that fancy talk." (I know he shouldn't have used old-fashioned words like that but it wasn't worth another scene about it.) "She said she doesn't know where to go next with that lad. One minute she's going to have him home and the next she wants him locked away somewhere in the country. Your Mum was taken really bad in the night ... that pain of hers really took hold. It's no wonder we're all so grouchy."

'So I ended up grovelling and offering to do all sorts of things which I haven't really got time for ... "Oh Dad I'm sorry about the pills, but I've got them now. I'll come round on Saturday to give you a break. I'm sorry I am in a rush now ... I just can't get everything done today, it's been one of those days." Well I just had to get back to do the dinner. So I got back late and started cooking dinner and it was all really getting on top of me. Jesse went right into the sandwich spread treatment and when Allan got in, I didn't let him get his coat off before I started on about my boss and the supermarket and my mum and what I should have done. "Well, one person's abuse is another one's discipline," he says. "My mum and dad were strict but it didn't do us any harm, at least we knew where we were. But I've got no time for teachers ... they were a sadistic bunch ... they used to have us line up to break a cane over our backsides. That's just the way it was in those days ... still I wouldn't want it to be like that for our lads. Although maybe if we were a bit tougher we wouldn't have someone sulking upstairs who can't tell the difference between no sandwich spread and the outbreak of World War III."

'Well, all evening the incident in the supermarket was going round in my head, and I was feeling terrible about Mum and Dad and how they can't really manage on their own for much longer. I really envy Allan and you your confidence. He is so easy with your parents but there's always been an edge with mine. My Dad was always having a go at my brother and he laid into him sometimes. It's no wonder he cleared off to Scotland and hardly ever gets in touch now. And when he used to spank me, well there was something a bit sexual about it that makes the hairs stand up on the back of my neck even to think about it ... so anyway I persuaded Allan to go for a drink ... to take me out of myself.

'Well, you'll never believe what happened ... we went up to the Anchor and we were talking about all this stuff and when we were on our way home, the rain had set in and it was bitter cold ... but it was sensible to walk so as not to drink and drive, but with such a bitter wind and all, and we almost literally bumped into the couple who were sitting next to us in the pub right up the High Street near the bus shelter,

bickering all evening they were and although I'm not one to mind
arguments, the way they were going at each other in public just isn't
right ... he starts yelling at her that she is a no-good slag and then
he started to hit her. Well, you know how Allan hates rows, he didn't
even stop to think but stepped right in between them. The bloke takes
one look at him and lands the punch he was aiming at his girlfriend
right on Allan, calling him a "black bastard" into the bargain. You'd
think she'd be grateful or sorry, but no, she just turns round and
shouted at both of us, "Get lost and mind your own business!"
Fortunately someone called the police and an ambulance because
there was blood everywhere. That's how come we ended up in
casualty ...'

'More coffee?'

2.1 What does the word 'abuse' mean to you?

It was certainly a bad Thursday. How seriously do you view the events
Pat describes?

Activity 2   **Responding to the case study**

Allow about 10 minutes   Read through the list below and note your reactions to the questions.

(a)   Is Pat being bullied by her boss?

(b)   Should the mum in the supermarket have slapped her daughter so
hard?

(c)   Should Pat have said something to the woman or was she right to
mind her own business?

(d)   Should Pat's dad call his nephew a 'mongol'?

(e)   How does Pat's mum feel when her husband says she'll have to go
into a home?

(f)   Does Pat's mum wet herself deliberately?

(g)   Did Pat neglect her mum by forgetting her medicine?

(h)   Should money come into the decision about whether Pat's mum goes
into a home?

(i)   Why does Allan feel OK about his parents' discipline but not his
teachers'?

(j)   Why might Pat's brother feel differently from Allan?

(k)   Should girls be hit the same as boys?

(l)   Is Pat just making it up about being spanked?

(m)   Is the fight between the couple from the pub a private matter?

Comment   As you might have guessed, there are no right answers to these
questions, but keep your comments to hand so that you can review them
to see whether you have changed your views as you work through the
unit.

Did you use the word 'abuse' to describe any of these incidents,
memories or relationships, or do you think it is too heavy handed? You
might feel that 'abuse' is not strong enough to describe the punch which
landed on Allan, which could be counted as an assault. But if that punch

had landed on the man's girlfriend, as was originally intended, would it have been called 'assault' or 'abuse'?

Williams (1993), who has done research with people with learning difficulties about their understanding and experiences of crime, thinks the word 'abuse' is too loosely used to be useful. He sees the term as a kind of ghetto word which only applies to certain groups of people and which minimises the seriousness of what can be violent, exploitative and often criminal acts. His view is that this is because the status (or lack of it) of people with learning difficulties allows crimes against them to be trivialised or played down. (Eastman, 1993, argues the same in relation to older people.) Using a universal term like 'abuse' is helpful in that it challenges us to ask why we apply different standards to people in particular settings or relationships. Below are three examples of different standards:

1   Is it less serious for a service user to be hit by another service user with 'challenging behaviour' than for you or me to be hit at home or at work? These are similar actions, but carried out in different circumstances. They would almost certainly lead to different sanctions and interventions.

2   I would not choose to live with a man who had a previous history of sexual offending. Yet if I were a woman with learning difficulties I might well find myself in this position without either my knowledge or assent.

3   If I were the victim of an assault I would not wish to continue to live or spend time alongside the person who had harmed me. If I were using services, I might have no option.

Certainly, the word 'abuse' tends to be used in relation to less powerful groups of people – as in child abuse, elder abuse, abuse of vulnerable adults, spouse abuse, racial abuse. But does the term 'abuse' add anything to our understanding of these situations? Here are some elements which usually feature in situations where the label 'abuse' is applied.

Abuse takes place within unequal relationships

There is often an unequal relationship involved in abuse within which one person (ab)uses their greater power:

* authority in the case of parents or teachers
* economic power in the case of Pat's boss, Mr Mitchell
* physical strength in the case of men who beat their wives or girlfriends.

Abuse is usually part of an ongoing relationship

The word 'abuse' tends to be used when harm is caused within an ongoing relationship rather than in the kind of one-off incident which happened to Allan.

Abuse is a deliberate action

Abuse is usually applied in situations where the abuser has intentionally misused his or her power.

This might lead you to question the way people use the word; for example, 'verbal abuse' as a description of a woman being taunted in the street by a group of youths sounds more serious than 'shouting' but less menacing than 'threatening'. What do you think?

2.2 Categories of abuse

Abuse comes in many shapes and sizes. Legal frameworks and policy documents issued by social services and other related agencies tend to categorise acts of abuse in slightly different ways. However, a consensus is emerging in the field of *adult abuse* to log cases under these headings:

- physical abuse
- sexual abuse
- psychological abuse
- financial abuse
- neglect.

Nevertheless, you might find variations. For example:

- Psychological abuse is sometimes referred to as emotional abuse or, more specifically, as verbal abuse.

- Abuse involving medication may have a section of its own, whereas in the classification used above, giving too much medication and sedating a person unnecessarily could be classed as 'physical abuse', while forgetting to give needed medication could be classed as 'neglect'.

- Neglect and negligence are sometimes separated out. Neglect implies a general 'lack of care' while negligence describes a more active 'carelessness' which you see when people are treated recklessly or allowed to take risks which have not been thought through.

Old people drugged to keep them quiet

Elderly people living in nursing and residential homes are being routinely prescribed sedative drugs to keep them quiet, says a damning report.

(*Community Care*, 15–21 May 1997)

Policeman jailed for stealing pensioner's cash

A policeman who befriended a lonely 79-year-old spinster then abused her trust by stealing £7,800 was jailed for 18 months yesterday.

(*Daily Telegraph*, 1 May 1997)

Turning into a nightmare

The case of a desperate woman who went to a charity for help, only for her trust to be abused

When Pat Bentley needed help for her tranquilliser addiction, she placed her trust in a centre run by a well-known charity. That trust was repaid with sexual exploitation by her counsellor.

(*Guardian*, 21 May 1997)

UNSPEAKABLE ACTS

Awareness is growing that disabled people are extremely vulnerable to physical and sexual abuse and often unable to tell others of their experiences.

(*Nursing Times*, 19 February 1992)

Carer who stole from school founder, 97, faces jail after judge condemns 'meanest' of crimes

Nurse's £33,000 betrayal of trust

A carer was convicted yesterday of taking more than £33,000 savings from the founder of a prestigious preparatory school during the two years before she died at the age of 97.

(*Daily Telegraph*, 1 May 1997)

Child abuse is categorised in the same way, with the exception of financial abuse. Child protection cases are classified into the following categories:

- neglect
- physical injury
- sexual abuse
- emotional abuse.

When a child is put on the at-risk register, types of abuse are noted under these headings.

The omission of a financial abuse category reflects the fact that children usually lack independent possessions. This bypasses some highly political issues. A child who goes without food because his or her parent has no money will be deemed to be the victim of parental neglect rather than poverty. In other words, the issue is located at an individual rather than a societal level. The more assets one has, the more vulnerable one is to financial abuse, so this is more often an issue in relation to vulnerable older people.

Income of the poorest families down 17% since 1979 as richest gain 62%

Official figures show third of children living in poverty

Poor get poorer

Changes in real income by decile group (10% bands of population), 1979–1991/92. Percentage change in income after housing costs.

Deciles		
1	10%	Poorest -17
2	10–20%	0
3	20–30%	6
4	30–40%	16
5	40–50%	23
6	50–60%	29
7	60–70%	33
8	70–80%	39
9	80–90%	46
10	90–100%	Wealthiest 62

(*Guardian*, 15 July 1994)

The legal definition of child abuse as set down in the Children Act 1989 is:

> ... *actual or likely harm to the child, where harm includes both ill-treatment (which includes sexual abuse and non-physical ill-treatment such as emotional abuse) and the impairment of health or development, health meaning physical or mental health, and development meaning physical, intellectual, emotional, social, or behavioural development.*

> (*The Children Act, 1989, s47(1)(b)*)

A professional worker or member of the public must report their concerns where they are confident that:

> ... *a child has suffered or is at risk of suffering significant harm from neglect, physical injury, sexual abuse or emotional abuse, or where a child has made a clear disclosure or allegation of abuse ...*

> (*Kent County Council Social Services, 1995/6, III.5*)

Now we are going to return to Pat's experiences to check how useful these labels and categories are in real life.

Activity 3 Identifying different forms of abuse

Allow about 10 minutes Go back through the list of questions in Activity 2. This time, instead of jotting down your own quick reactions, note whether you think the incidents and relationships could be interpreted as abuse (either child or adult). If so, do they fit into the categories listed below? List each case under the appropriate heading. Where they don't seem to fit, make a brief note.

(a) Physical

(b) Sexual

(c) Psychological

(d) Financial

(e) Neglect

Comment   I listed:

Physical

- the little girl in the supermarket
- Allan abused by his teachers
- Allan by the man from the pub
- Pat's brother by her father
- possibly Pat by her father but I didn't know whether to put this down as sexual instead (or maybe both physical and sexual).

Psychological (which I thought was mostly verbal)

- Mr Mitchell, Pat's boss, shouting and maybe bullying if he is deliberately out to get at her
- Pat's father towards her mother because she had been left wet and uncomfortable
- Pat's father calling Derek a 'mongol'
- the man in the pub towards his girlfriend.

Neglect

- perhaps when Pat forgot her mother's medicine
- when Pat's mother was left wet and uncomfortable.

Things that didn't fit the categories

I didn't like the fact that the decision about whether Pat's mother should go into a home was influenced by the finances of Pat's family and her son's wish to go to college, although I could quite see how this would come about. If this had been a firm decision I might have put it down as 'financial abuse', but it was just a thought and I didn't think Pat would act against her mother's interests if things got worse at home.

I wondered if the man who hit Allan had been influenced by the fact that he is black. I thought he had hit him because he had dared to interfere between him and his girlfriend but there may have been a racial element to it. But then I realised that racism would be more to do with his motivation than with what he actually did, so I wasn't sure whether it should be a separate category or not and I left it under the 'physical' heading.

I also questioned whether I should put Allan down as having been physically abused by his parent(s). Although he seemed to have defined it as discipline, it struck me as odd that I might categorise Pat's brother as having been physically abused and not Allan, even though they may have experienced the same things.

Although I thought Pat neglected her mother on this occasion by forgetting the medicine, I also had questions about this. Mostly the word 'abuse' describes situations where someone has done something harmful. Would you use 'abuse' to describe Pat's failure to get her mother's medication? Because you know Pat didn't *mean* to forget her mother's pills, would you let her off the hook? Can we abuse someone without meaning to? If we say that Pat was neglectful, how do we feel about her brother, who doesn't visit at all? We have already seen that there are pressures and expectations which might lead Pat, as her parents' only daughter, to become their main carer, even though she has plenty of family responsibilities and financial pressures in her own life.

Did you come up with any other 'types' of abuse or problems in fitting these incidents or events to the headings?

'He tripped on the stairs.'

There's no excuse for child abuse. Anywhere. Ever.
With your support the NSPCC can help stop the violence.

NSPCC

Some of these questions will be revisited later in the unit. At this point, however, the last item in the comment, about Pat's 'neglect', demands further consideration. If we are going to make a judgment about someone who is doing a lot but making mistakes or overlooking things, what is our view of people who opt out altogether? Stevenson, whose research into abuse spans over 25 years, says in a report comparing responses to abuse of children with that of older people:

> ... we are some way from being able to devise preventive strategies for elder abuse because ... there is quite a high degree of moral confusion about the status of adult relationships.

> (Stevenson, 1996, p. 23)

In other words, it is hard to say what 'duty' Pat (or her brother) has to her mother in these circumstances and this makes it harder to judge her actions or her failures. A similar issue arises in the context of residential care, where abusive acts are more likely to be committed by direct care staff and at times when more senior staff have gone off duty (see Sundram, 1984). If you are left on duty alone without adequate support to meet the needs of all the people nominally in your care, who is the one doing the neglecting – you, or those who have failed to staff the service adequately? You'll recognise this as the sort of question addressed when accountability was discussed in Block 5. It is certainly a question to ask in cases such as the 'bedroom abuse' described in Lee-Treweek in the Reader (Chapter 25).

Limitations to these categories

There are advantages to agreeing a single system of labels. If every area uses a different scheme it is not possible to monitor practice and make comparisons across different agencies. However, there are problems in thinking about abuse in the way I have outlined. It focuses attention rather narrowly on a certain type of act and this may simplify our thinking too much. It can obscure the complex dynamics which exist in abusive relationships and so lead us to see abuse as a single act rather than as an ongoing process – one which often includes some elements of a 'cover-up', or of cycles of abusing followed by promises that it won't happen again. Also, in practice the types often overlap. In a recent study of cases of adult abuse reported in two authorities over one year, multiple abuses were documented in at least a fifth of cases (Brown and Stein, 1998). For example, a member of staff might use physical violence, or the threat of it, to coerce an adult with learning difficulties to engage in, or maintain secrecy about, a sexual act and it is hard to see how such an act could fail to cause psychological harm. This kind of overlap has been documented in relation to child protection cases as well (see Farmer and Owen, 1995); and similarly with domestic violence, which is described as involving:

> *... a variable combination of physical, emotional, sexual and psychological abuse within a relationship context. The violence can be actual, threatened or attempted, and is usually committed by adult men against adult women with whom they are, or have been, in a relationship. As a crime of interpersonal violence it is about the use of humiliation, threats and/or force to maintain power and control over the victim and other members of the household.*

> *(Holder et al., 1994, p. 5)*

This kind of pervasive abuse within a relationship does not fit neatly into any of the boxes, but spans all of them. Moreover, as we saw in Unit 22, when abuse takes place within a service it may be important to be alert to the nature of the whole regime or wider system, rather than a single act or the behaviour of an individual abuser.

2.3 Evaluating seriousness

Whatever words are used, the term 'abuse' has many different dimensions. Defining abuse isn't only a matter of categorising acts into types as you did in Activity 3, but is also about judging when something is serious enough to warrant action. We will be considering this at length in relation to physical abuse of children and sexual abuse of adults with learning difficulties. The Children Act 1989 adds the notion of seriousness into definitions of abuse by stipulating that for action to be taken the child must be at risk of 'significant' harm. For adults there is no equivalent legislation, although local authorities are trying to establish common frameworks. A measure of seriousness in relation to adults might be how far any abuse constitutes a criminal act, but even that is interpreted 'flexibly' by individual practitioners and police officers; also at an institutional level by the Criminal Prosecution Service, which uses a 'public interest' criterion as one factor in deciding whether or not to prosecute particular cases.

When we use the word 'abuse' we are essentially making a value judgment. We are saying that an act, or series of acts, in a relationship is intolerable. It is a judgment made from the outside by a third party or agency and one which is liable to change over time, and in different contexts, cultures and settings. We make judgments in individual cases against the background of prevailing economic and cultural attitudes and we have to act on these judgments in the light of public consensus about how we should relate to each other.

ARE YOU IN AN ABUSIVE RELATIONSHIP?

Signs of abuse

● Your boyfriend constantly puts you down and tells you you're ugly/stupid/no good in bed.

● You believe him and feel grateful that he suffers you.

● He hits you. But he's so sorry afterwards you let him get away with it, and even cover up for him.

● He says he'll change – but he never does.

What to do if you think you are in an abusive relationship

● Recognise the problem. If he's violent there's nothing you can do to help. It's up to him to change. Even if you have a rocky relationship, that doesn't excuse his use of violence.

● Tell a friend, or member of your family about him. Opening up will be a relief, and it's good to get another perspective.

● Get practical advice – try one of the organisations we've suggested [in the margin]. They'll help with practical matters, too, such as a place to take refuge if you're living with him.

● Take a deep breath and walk out. Don't wait until the next time he hits you. You might end up seriously hurt. ...

● Don't go rushing back to him, even if your feelings for one another are still there. Wait a few months and get some counselling. If you really want to make a go of it, make sure he realises he has a problem and has done something about it.

Women's Aid National Helpline: 0345 023468 (Mon–Fri, 10am–5pm).

REFUGE: 0181 995 4430. A 24-hour crisis line that can help you find a safe place to stay and offers legal advice and counselling.

Police stations now have domestic violence or vulnerable persons units. Call your local station for details.

(*19 Magazine*, 8–13 December 1996)

Activity 4   Evaluating seriousness

Allow about 20 minutes   When concerns are voiced about abuse practitioners have to weigh up one factor against another to decide whether a particular situation warrants intervention. In this activity you are going to look at some of the factors to be taken into account to arrive at these judgments.

Consider each of the incidents listed. Put a (1) by the one you consider the most serious and then rank the others down to (9), the least worrying.

(a)   Boss shouts at woman in front of other workers for losing something.

(b)   Mother slaps little girl hard on leg in supermarket.

(c)   Teacher canes whole class of boys on backside.

(d)   Daughter forgets frail older mother's medicine, causing her pain.

(e)   Husband threatens wife with going into a home when she wets herself.

(f)   Man calls his girlfriend a 'slag' in public.

(g)   Father slaps teenage son for not doing his schoolwork (Allan and Pat's brother).

(h)   Father spanks daughter on bottom over his knee.

(i)   One man punches another in the face outside the pub.

Now look at your list and think about how you made your judgments. Did you base them on the harm which had actually been done to the victim (in which case Pat's forgetting to get the medicine had caused as much discomfort as the young mother's slapping her child in the supermarket)? Did you take into account the intentions of the person who was responsible for the abuse or the nature of their relationship? For each of the criteria below, take a different coloured pencil and note down a new set of numbers, ranking the incidents in a new order. Notice which ones change place when you consider the incidents from a different point of view.

Criteria:

*   how harmful the act was
*   how harmful it was in the short term and in the longer term
*   whether it was done on purpose or by accident.

Do you think there are other important criteria besides these three? Write them down.

Comment   You might like to compare your criteria with the list developed by Brown and Stein to assist staff in evaluating seriousness:

*   How vulnerable is the victim?
*   How extensive is the abuse? For example, if financial abuse, how much money? If physical abuse, what damage has been done?
*   Was it a one-off incident or part of a long-standing or repeated pattern?
*   What impact is it having on the vulnerable person's well-being?
*   Are other people being damaged or threatened by it ... for example children or other family members, other residents in residential care or onlookers?
*   What were the intentions of the alleged abuser ... has it been done deliberately ... was it planned ... is there any evidence that the person actively targeted this person or other vulnerable people?
*   Is what has happened against the law ... can legal action be taken, or other formal steps such as disciplinary action or a formal complaint or action under the Registered Homes Act?
*   Will it happen again to this vulnerable person if action is not taken? Sexual abuse, for example, is very likely to be repeated.
*   Might it happen again to other vulnerable people at risk ... for example other service users/residents, children or other adults in the household?

(Adapted from Brown and Stein, 1998)

I doubt if you got all these, but hope you found at least some common ground.

In the guidance developed by Brown and Stein, workers were asked to separate out issues of *evidence* from issues of *seriousness*. It is often difficult to get clear *evidence* about what may be going on but this should not be taken as a signal that the situation is not potentially serious.

Key points

*   Evaluating the seriousness of abuse is complex.
*   Factors to take into account include the extent of the harm caused, the context and the perpetrator's intent.
*   Future risk is also a key issue in deciding whether action is called for.

2.4 Context as part of definition

We have seen that you can place a potentially abusive act in a category and within that you can place each act on a continuum of severity in terms of the harm it causes. So, for example, you might decide that an injury which caused bruising was slightly less serious than one which led to abrasions, broken bones or permanent tissue damage. But that wouldn't be the end of the story, would it? Did you rank the assault on Allan as more or less serious than the incident with the little girl? While the severity of the act itself makes a difference, so do the intentions of the perpetrator, the power differential and the vulnerability of the victim. Different situations are 'constructed' or interpreted differently depending on the relationship between the people concerned; for example whether they are parent and child or husband and wife. The context has to be taken into account to judge whether any specific incident separately or cumulatively crosses a threshold of acceptability. For example, you might decide that the incident in the supermarket is not in itself bad enough to warrant taking action but you might want to check if this kind of thing has happened before; if it has it would be possible for something quite minor to tip the balance and make you take action.

Thinking about these issues will almost certainly lead you to reflect on your own upbringing and your beliefs about how to raise children or what constitutes a happy marriage/partnership. You might also reflect on your attitude to whether the 'state' or caring services such as health or social services have any remit or responsibility to step in. You may think these issues are private and no one's business but your own. On the other hand, you may think the government should protect children or vulnerable adults, regulate punishment in school or at home, and legislate against fights in public and private places. You may have different views about what is right in schools or at home, between neglect in a person's own flat or in residential care (confusingly also called 'a home'), about a fight involving strangers and one involving a couple. As you complete this section, reflect for a moment on whether you tend to make different judgments about the same behaviours depending on whether they take place in the public or the private sphere.

Key points

- The word 'abuse' is not very accurate. It tends to play down some situations while overreacting to others.

- Abusive acts can be categorised, for example as physical, sexual, psychological or financial, and placed on a continuum of seriousness.

- Different types of abuse often occur within the same abusive relationship.

- The same act may be treated differently according to whether it took place in public or private.

Section 3
Child protection: a worked example

When we left Bernice she was washing up the coffee cups after her discussion with Pat. Since that conversation she has felt quite upset because, although she didn't tell Pat at the time, she knows the mother in the emerald green jacket. The young woman is called Sue and she brings her daughter to the playgroup which Bernice runs. She is not a single mother, as Pat had assumed, but lives with her partner, her daughter's father. Bernice has been worried for some time about the way Sue disciplines her daughter – it isn't that she is 'firm', it is more that she is erratic. She seems to take little notice of her daughter's play and to ignore her when she comes up to show off her pictures, then will suddenly butt in harshly when a more gentle reminder might work just as well.

While Pat was pondering her duties as a citizen and how uncomfortable she would have been 'reporting' the incident she witnessed, Bernice has clear duties as a professional child-care worker and knows that she should report the matter to social services if she is in any doubt. But her 'common sense' tells her that lots of children are smacked occasionally without long-term harm. She knows that families go through bad patches but their kids turn out OK in the end. Also, she wonders what would happen if she *did* report it. Would Sue just stop coming? Is she exaggerating the matter and should she allow what she has been told 'off the record' by Pat to influence her judgment?

One evening Bernice sat down absent-mindedly and wrote the following list. These were the questions she turned over in her mind:

> - Is this physical abuse or does it not count because it's her mum smacking her?
> - Is it bad enough for me to report it?
> - How 'normal' is it? At the moment I think it is quite extreme but does this happen in all families?
> - How long has it been going on and how often does it happen? I've seen four instances that I can think of and Pat has seen one. Is Sue just going through a bad time?
> - Does she make up for it in other ways? Perhaps she has good points as a mother as well.
> - How could this kind of discipline affect the little girl in the long run?
> - What would social services do and would it make it worse? Perhaps we should offer Sue more days at playgroup instead of labelling her as a problem.

These concerns are very typical. An overview of recent research compiled by the Dartington Social Research Unit (as part of an initiative by the government to redirect the emphasis from investigation to support in child protection matters) points to these kinds of considerations which professionals weigh up when making judgments about when to intervene:

- *moral/legal concerns ... is it wrong?*
- *pragmatic concerns ... can we help or will we make it worse?*
- *concerns about outcome ... how much damage will this do in the longer run?*

(Dartington Social Research Unit, 1995, p. 17)

These sum up Bernice's concerns. Bernice knew she would have to make up her mind whether to speak to a social worker or not, and decided to go to the library on Saturday morning to see if she could find any books or articles which would help her to clarify her thoughts.

Key points

- Anyone working with children has a clear duty to report concerns about child protection issues.

- In deciding whether to intervene workers make a judgment about whether particular ways of behaving are 'right' or 'wrong'.

- Knowing what will happen in the longer term may be part of the equation.

- Workers also consider whether their intervention could help or may make things worse.

3.1 Child 'abuse' or just 'discipline'

It is clear from the story above that there are many different beliefs about what is acceptable behaviour, especially within the family. As a society our attitudes towards children are inconsistent. On the one hand, we have a complex child protection system within which to operate (which we don't have for vulnerable adults), but at the same time children are the only group not included within the general legal framework relating to assault. The police were called to the scene when Allan was punched in the nose by the man from the pub but no one called the police to the little girl in the supermarket. Parents are, and until recently teachers were, 'allowed' or 'legitimated' to use physical force to control children's behaviour. In many circles such behaviour is approved of and political and church leaders are not afraid to own up to 'smacking' their children.

At the time of writing teachers in state schools in the UK are not allowed to use corporal punishment, but teachers in independent schools are, although this is shortly to be tested before the European Court.

Blair admits smacking his children – and feeling remorse

Alice Thomson Political Reporter

Tony Blair, who has always claimed to be 'tough on crime and tough on the causes of crime', has been applying the same principles at home.

The Labour leader admitted yesterday that he smacked his children and believed corporal punishment was an appropriate tool to help to maintain discipline. The admission to Parent Magazine has delighted Right-wing Tories who are thrilled that the Labour leader has joined a select band of parliamentary smackers, including Virginia Bottomley and Baroness Thatcher ...

(The Times, 6 June 1996)

How 'typical' is smacking?

As Allan said, 'one person's abuse is another person's discipline'. Many people think that smacking children is acceptable in certain circumstances, perhaps depending on:

- the relationship of the people involved
- whether they would see the hitting as 'deserved'
- how they would view the rights or role of the person doing the hitting to discipline or control the person on the receiving end.

An ICM poll done for the *Guardian* showed considerable public support for corporal punishment of children and young people.

Table 1   ICM Poll Chart

	Percentage strongly supporting corporal punishment	Percentage slightly supporting corporal punishment	Total percentage supporting corporal punishment
By parents of own children	50	31	81
By child carers, nannies, other relatives	19	26	45
By class teachers on pupils	40	27	67
By head teachers on pupils	47	24	71
By courts following a criminal conviction	55	15	70

(Source: *Guardian*, 7 November 1996, p. 9)

You can see from this that it is by no means clear where, in the public mind, the line falls between discipline and abuse. A recent American study confirmed Bernice's impression that it is quite normal for mothers to punish even very young children by smacking them. Socolar and Stein (1995) surveyed mothers attending two clinics about their attitudes and it was found that almost one-fifth (19 per cent) thought that there were times when spanking was appropriate for a child under one year of age and this went up to three-quarters who believed it appropriate to smack children between the ages of one and three. Forty-two per cent had smacked their own child in the past week. In terms of severity of punishment, 8 per cent believed it was appropriate to smack hard enough to leave a mark and 19 per cent to use an object (such as a hairbrush or belt) and not just a slap with the hand. This study reported that girls were smacked more often than boys and that mothers who had been smacked themselves smacked their children more often. Mothers attending the inner city clinic believed in smacking, and smacked their children more often than the better-off mothers from the private clinic.

Study skills: Reading tables

Have you developed the habit of stopping to read tables rather than skipping over them? You should have found the one on the previous page quite easy after all the practice you have had. Just to test yourself:

- Can you see what proportion of people did not support any kind of corporal punishment?

- Is there more support for corporal punishment by parents than by the courts?

- Trying to generalise from the table, do people think just *anybody* should be allowed to administer corporal punishment? If not, what type of person should it be?

Here are my answers:

- The highest overall levels of support are for corporal punishment by parents. If 81 per cent of people support it, then 19 per cent don't support it (and presumably don't support it when administered by others either).

- A tricky one, since there are slightly more people *strongly* in favour of corporal punishment by the courts, but more people *overall* who support parental corporal punishment. So there isn't an absolutely clear answer.

- All the categories here are people who might be 'in charge' of children. But there is quite a lot more doubt about child carers, nannies and other relatives. It seems that the traditional 'authority figures' – parents, teachers and representatives of the law – are the ones seen as legitimate corporal punishers.

Do you feel you are getting pretty good at drawing sense out of figures now?

Key points

- Smacking young children is accepted by most people as a reasonable form of discipline.

- Smacking can range from a light slap to hitting with an object, such as a hairbrush or belt.

- Smacking is widespread.

Is ordinary smacking a form of child abuse?

The first reading Bernice really got her teeth into was a debate about smacking which looked at the arguments for and against this 'ordinary' routine smacking of children within their families. This is reproduced in Offprint 32 which is taken from an American book, *Debating Children's Lives*, edited by Mason and Gambill (1994, pp. 195–223).

In the preface the editors explain the advantages they see in presenting issues in a debate format. They say it allows readers to see both sides of an issue clearly. But they also warn of the risk that the ideas may become polarised, so that people feel they can only take an extreme view.

Study skills: Engaging with academic debates

When you study at university level you enter a world of debates. Academic knowledge advances through the clash of different ideas. People deliberately present their positions in an 'extreme' form, so that the logical differences between ideas stand out clearly. Then they search for evidence and lines of analysis which will tilt the balance towards one theory and against another. But the debate only works in this 'constructive', knowledge-building way because it is conducted in an orderly fashion according to established rules. The idea is that you read other people's arguments carefully and respond to them point by point, through logical analysis. You are supposed to present your own case 'objectively', keeping your personality, values and preferences to one side. Ideas are meant to be judged on their own merits, regardless of their practical implications, and independently of who puts them forward.

Outside the academic world, in society at large, there are also many debates. But these are not necessarily conducted in a disciplined way. You 'win' the argument by capturing popular support or getting the backing of powerful people. Appealing to emotions, playing on people's loyalties, shouting loudly and denigrating your opponent are all part of the game, as are compromising and 'fudging the issues' to reach a resolution.

You need to develop skill in following an academic debate, as writers on different sides weave together arguments and evidence to support their particular points of view. You also need to be able to detect when they are *not* following the rules of academic argument – sneaking in emotional appeals, fudged arguments, and so on. The debate you are about to read is an excellent opportunity, both to see how academic writers battle for their own ideas, and to notice when the rules of academic debate are being broken.

I chose this offprint material for three reasons.

- It sets out some strong arguments for and against the use of physical punishment.

- It shows you some of the kinds of evidence which are used.

- It gives an idea of the role of academic debate in relation to public debate and the development of social policy.

Activity 5   Is corporal punishment by parents abuse?

Allow about 10 minutes   Before you start to read Offprint 32 I want you to do some homework! I want you to monitor your own views on the topic as we work through the debate to see if you shift at all having read some of the arguments. The question under debate in Offprint 32 is:

'Should the use of corporal punishment by parents be considered child abuse?'

A note of caution: they use the term 'anti' to mean 'against spanking', not against the question. Also they use the term 'naysayers', i.e. those who say no to spanking but not to the question as it is expressed here. If you answer yes, you would be against spanking; if you answer no you would be in favour of it. Before you read the offprint, register your own 'gut instinct' position. Don't agonise – just tick the point which most nearly represents your view.

Yes, corporal punishment is abuse	Yes, but I have some reservations	I don't know or can't make up my mind	No, but I have some reservations	No, corporal punishment isn't abuse

Comment   Have your response at hand as you work through this section. As you consider the points raised by different contributors, use the same headings to monitor if and how your views change. You'll be reminded to do this after each activity in this section.

Defining terms

It is possible that you found Activity 5 difficult because we haven't defined our terms. What do we mean by 'corporal punishment'? I can't ask you to indicate whether you agree with spanking children if that varies wildly from hitting a child with a hairbrush on his or her bare bottom until blood is drawn, to lightly tapping a child with your hand across his or her open palm.

So before going any further, consider what *you* meant by corporal punishment? What image came into your mind? If you agreed with 'it', what were you in favour of and if you disagreed, what were you disagreeing with? You will see that the contributors to Offprint 32 all agree that some forms of physical punishment are definitely abusive, for example if it is out of control or involves hitting with an object such as a belt or stick. Their debate is about 'mild spanking' and Larzelere defines this as 'a maximum of two slaps on the buttocks with an open hand'. Straus defines corporal punishment as the 'use of physical force with the intention of causing a child to experience pain but not injury'.

Activity 6   **Reviewing your position**

Allow about 5 minutes   So now where do you stand? In the light of the definition of corporal punishment as 'mild spanking', tick the box which represents your views now.

Yes, even ordinary spanking is abuse	Yes, but I have some reservations	I don't know or can't make up my mind	No, but I have some reservations	No, ordinary spanking isn't abuse

Comment   Have you shifted? If so, this makes the point that often in a debate it isn't the actual evidence that is being weighed up but the initial emotional response to the words which are being used. Part of the debate is about agreeing what the words mean, a bit like an army agreeing 'terms of engagement'.

Study skills: Understanding the importance of frames of reference

An academic argument involves making a sequence of connected points within a frame of reference. (When you write a TMA the title provides the main frame of reference.) A debate between different arguments can only take place if all sides are prepared to work within a common frame of reference (i.e. what the debate is 'all about', including the meanings of key words). In practice, a lot of the art of debating is trying to drag the frame of reference in your direction to give your arguments a better chance. Already we can glimpse this here. Terms like 'mild spanking' and 'two slaps on the buttocks' set up a frame of reference where punishment is an orderly, controlled, benign action; whereas using 'physical force' to cause 'pain' sets a frame in which punishment involves a strong person intimidating a weak one.

Do you remember the discussion about the 'construction of social reality', in Unit 4, Section 4.1? Here again we have physical reality – the slap – giving rise to different constructions of social reality – mild spanking or physical assault. Which way the debate goes in the public realm has a lot to do with which of these constructions dominates. As you will read later in an extract from the Dartington Report, 'Society continually reconstructs definitions of maltreatment which sanction intervention' (Dartington Social Research Unit, 1995, p. 15).

The debate

Now it is time to get to grips with the debate. The first contribution is by Murray Straus, who identifies himself as a researcher and sociologist; we do not know if he is a parent himself.

Activity 7   Reading Murray Straus

Allow about 30 minutes   This activity is in three parts.

(a)   Straus is arguing that corporal punishment *should* be considered as child abuse. Before you read, try to anticipate the questions he might be answering and jot them down.

(b)   When you have done that, read and make notes on his arguments (pages 113–9 of the Offprints Book).

(c)   Then make some notes on what evidence he uses to support his arguments.

Comment   (a)   Anticipating the questions

I thought Straus might be asking:
- Does physical punishment work?
- Does it do damage – in the short or the longer term?

Did you think of any other questions? If so, you could use these as headings to help you make notes as you read. I also wondered what kind of evidence he would produce to persuade us – he could just say 'well, I think it is wrong', or he could try to prove whether people who are physically punished go on to do this or suffer from that, using proper research studies. I put another heading for evidence so that I could make a note of the kind of information he uses to support his ideas.

(b)   Notes on his arguments

These are my notes:

He starts by asking if the risks are greater than alternative methods of discipline. Then he asks:

Does it work?

- Nearly everyone does it.
- It is no better than alternatives such as explaining, or removing the child.

Does it do damage?

- Incurs risk of psychological damage.
- Increases likelihood of juvenile delinquency and assaults on others.
- Teaches child to hit more.
- Increases spouse abuse.
- Increases likelihood that person will abuse own children.
- Increases likelihood of drink problems, suicide risk and depression.

(c)   What kind of evidence does he produce?

- Provides analysis of over 2,000 families.
- Doesn't provide anything on how effective it is; only on the longer-term risks.
- Doesn't say when or why parents do it.

Has he persuaded you to change your mind? Mark your position on the five-point scale again to show where you stand now.

Yes, ordinary spanking is abuse	Yes, but I have some reservations	I don't know or can't make up my mind	No, but I have some reservations	No, ordinary spanking isn't abuse

Study skills: Reading graphs

In the offprint you have seen a number of graphs. Look back at Figure 1.

The people being studied in Figure 1 were divided into two broad groups according to whether or not there was violence between their parents. Each group was then divided into eight groups according to how many times their parents physically punished them during their teen years. You can see the eight groupings marked along the bottom of the diagram, ranging from 'None' to '30+'. Then for each of the 16 groups (two lots of eight) the proportion of men involved in wife assault was worked out. This is shown as a 'probability' figure. The scale shows probabilities ranging from 0.6 at the high end to 0.1 at the low end. (The highest probability figure you can have is 1.0, which means that the thing you are concerned with is absolutely certain to happen; the lowest is 0, which means that there is no likelihood at all that it will happen.)

So let's look at the bottom dot on the left. We can see from the label on the sloping line that this is a group whose parents were not violent to each other. Looking down to the horizontal axis we see 'None', so they were also never hit by their parents in their teens. Looking to the left we see that for the men in this group the probability of their being involved in wife assault was between .1 and .2 (say about .14). This is a lowish probability (about a 14 per cent chance). The next dot to the right is the group who were hit once by their parents in their teens. As you can see, their probability of being involved in wife assault was a bit higher (say .16). Moving up to the other end of the line, we see that those who had been hit 30 times or more had about a .3 probability of being involved in wife assault (30 per cent). Since the dots rise steadily up the line, it is obvious that the more times boys were hit in their teens the more likely they are to be involved in wife assault when they grow up. In other words, there is a strong 'correlation' between the two (you met correlations in Unit 21).

You can read the other line in exactly the same way. This is the group who experienced violence between their parents. At the left end of the line you can see that even those who were never hit by their parents in their teens have around a 30 per cent likelihood of being involved in wife assault, rising to around 50 per cent for those who were hit a lot by their parents. We can see that both violence between parents and being hit frequently by their parents in their teens were directly related to men being involved in wife assault later in life.

The other graphs are all of the same kind. If you read the labels and again start at the bottom dot on the left, you will be able to work out what they are telling you.

Correlations and causation

The fact that there is a strong correlation between the frequency of being hit by parents as a teenager and later involvement in wife assault does not prove that one *causes* the other. For example, you might argue that people are born with personalities ranging from very mild and compliant to very confrontational and aggressive. In that case the milder, more compliant people might be less likely to arouse their parents to hit them *and* also less likely to be involved in wife assault, and the confrontational, aggressive ones might be more likely to be hit by parents and be involved in wife assault. So the fact that being hit more often by parents goes with being more likely to be involved in wife assault may be because *both* are 'caused' by *something else* (e.g. inborn personality). This is not an argument in favour of personality as an explanation, just a demonstration that correlation never proves causation. When two measures correlate, you can never say that one 'causes' the other. (The higher the harbour boats rise, the smaller the beach gets, but it isn't the boats rising that causes the beach to get smaller.) All you can say is that the two vary together.

Next you are going to read a contribution by Robert Larzelere, who also identifies himself as a social scientist and researcher; again he does not say if he is a parent. I am going to use the same headings to make notes on his arguments. I expect him to focus more on whether punishment works in the immediate setting but we will see ...

Activity 8   Reading Robert Larzelere

Allow about 20 minutes   Now read and make notes on Robert Larzelere's contribution on pages
     119–23 of Offprint 32, using the headings from the previous activity.

Comment   Does it work?

- Larzelere says it works to back up a 'time out' (i.e. sending a child to his or her room) approach.

- In combination with reasoning, it reduces fighting and disobedience.

- It increases the effectiveness of reasoning alone next time – I suppose by making a child more likely to 'listen'.

- But he is talking about spanking 2–6 year-olds, not teenagers as Straus does.

Does it do damage?

- No, he says it fits into authoritative parenting, which is good.

- He notes increased risk of aggression but says it is minimal.

- He says banning it would do damage and cites Sweden, where banning spanking led to increased reports of child abuse; he thinks parents who can't spank are more likely to lose control.

- He says it is culturally insensitive to ban it.

What kind of evidence does he produce?

- Lots of studies but doesn't really explain them; mostly evidence for it working rather than about long-term effects.

Bernice picked up on the point about cultural diversity because it raised issues for her: coming from an African-Caribbean background she has often been aware that she and Allan have different views about discipline and strictness and feel differently from Pat about family matters. In the past she had put this down to individual difference but she resolved to look into it further.

So where do you stand now? Has this part of the offprint caused you to shift again, perhaps back towards the 'no' position and more accepting of mild spanking of children and/or teenagers? Mark your position on the five-point scale.

Yes, ordinary spanking is abuse	Yes, but I have some reservations	I don't know or can't make up my mind	No, but I have some reservations	No, ordinary spanking isn't abuse

Finally, there is a contribution by John Rosemond – he is a psychologist and runs a centre for 'affirmative parenting', and he tells us he is a parent himself.

Activity 9	**Reading John Rosemond**
Allow about 20 minutes	Now read and make notes on the last contribution (pages 123–6), using the same headings again.

Comment

Does it work?

- Rosemond says usually it is used ineffectively, that it should be used not as a back-up but as a prelude to some other action, that spanking should be 'a first resort'.

Does it do damage?

- Says not.

What kind of evidence does he produce?

- He calls those he disagrees with 'pseudo-intellectual, politically correct megalomaniacs' and says they have 'swollen egos'.

- He dismisses 'all' the research studies, saying they 'stink'.

- He uses his own children as an example.

Now where are you?

Yes, ordinary spanking is abuse	Yes, but I have some reservations	I don't know or can't make up my mind	No, but I have some reservations	No, ordinary spanking isn't abuse

Look back over your position at various stages of the debate – did you come to these readings with a fairly firm view or an open mind? Have you been persuaded to change your mind by their arguments or to think about new issues? What new information or ideas have they introduced?

3.2 Science and values

The readings left Bernice unsettled. She had several concerns.

First, the contributors took for granted that there is agreement about how we want children to behave: for example, Larzelere says that he is aiming at compliance where another person might value independence of thought or spontaneity more highly.

Second, they were not all talking about the same thing. Straus was mostly talking about spanking teenagers whereas Larzelere was talking about children from two to six. Larzelere advocated spanking as a last resort and Rosemond as a first.

Third, the authors confused the issue by bringing their own attitudes towards and versions of 'science' into the debate. Rosemond turned it into a personal attack on people who disagree with spanking and claimed it was a matter of personal responsibility rather than social policy.

Fourth, the evidence cited is variable. Straus used a sample of 2,000 families, whereas Rosemond generalised from his own experience with his own two children (from whom we do not hear). Later in the original paper Straus responded to Rosemond by stating the case for science. He says:

> *The difference between scientists ... and 'zealots' ... is that scientists test their assumptions and are willing to let the findings of scientific tests have the last word. My research was designed to give the assumption that all spanking is abusive a chance to be either supported or disproved.*

(Mason and Gambill, 1994, p. 221)

Study skills: Not playing by the rules

As you were reading the offprint, did you recognise that Rosemond breaks the rules of academic debate and instead adopts the tone of a general public debate? Far from taking the other side's arguments seriously and analysing them point by point, he call his opponents names, sweeps aside their research with a dismissive gesture, and tries to draw us into identifying with his own parental relationship with his children. Although Straus and Larzelere disagree with each other, they are prepared to talk within the same academic frame of reference. Rosemond is not interested in playing that game. He knows that the winner of an academic debate still has to win support within wider public debate if they want to influence policy. So he opts out of the academic debate and goes straight for the public/political game.

The status of science

Incidentally, the word 'science' is bandied about here. Science is one particular kind of academic discourse which tends to carry high status in public debates. If you say an argument is 'academic' that unfortunately tends to be interpreted as meaning 'irrelevant', whereas if you say it is 'scientific' it is likely to be taken seriously. Science is supposed to be concerned with carrying out experiments to test theories. However, in the social 'sciences' it is often not possible to carry out experiments. Instead, they tend to rely on detailed and systematic data gathering. So when displaying its 'scientific' side, social science tends to present graphs and tables of numbers, as Straus does here. Larzelere quotes numbers too, from a range of different studies. These figures are used by both to try to swing the academic debate their way, but they are also being displayed here to lend credibility to claims of being 'scientific'. Straus makes clear that he thinks scientific arguments are more open-minded and fair. However, there are times when scientific arguments are worryingly narrow, as for example with Bowlby's account of the baby-bound mother (Unit 1), and eugenicists' proposals to restrict certain people's rights to have children (Unit 16). Science has a very important role to play in debates about policies, but it should never be assumed to deliver simply 'the truth'.

The quality of the evidence is not the only issue. There is another debate going on here about whether the state has any right to interfere in the way people treat each other. In this case it is about parents and children but it could also be stated in relation to men and women or carers and their elderly relatives. Setting rules in the private sphere can be characterised as an encroachment on the freedom of individuals in their homes and personal relationships. In this case it would limit the freedom of parents to act as they think fit. But the limits it would set are on the more powerful partner in these exchanges: on the parents not the children, the potentially violent spouse, the carer not the cared for. You could argue that by limiting the freedom of these people you can extend the freedom of the less powerful person.

So at the end of the debate where do you stand now?

Yes, I think ordinary spanking is child abuse	Yes, but I have some reservations	I don't know or can't make up my mind	No, but I have some reservations	No, I do not think ordinary spanking is child abuse

Before leaving the debate let's review the way this exchange has been managed by the three contributors. Their debate focused on three main areas:

1   Whether corporal punishment works in terms of controlling behaviour in an immediate sense (making children more 'compliant' and obedient).

2   Whether it has harmful side effects in the longer term, for example by teaching children that it is OK to hit people, especially if they love them, or by leading to depression and other psychological problems.

3   The rightness and effect of introducing a blanket 'ban' which interferes with the right of individual parents to act according to their own values.

Study skills: The social science disciplines

One reason why our three debaters disagree is that they come from different social science 'disciplines'. Psychologists, sociologists, economists and political scientists develop their own kinds of arguments. They work from different kinds of questions and seek out different kinds of evidence. So answers from one discipline don't necessarily make a lot of sense in relation to the questions in a different discourse. Psychological enquiry tends to focus on what goes on inside a person, for example exploring how a child's behaviour changes in response to a particular regime of discipline and punishment. Sociology looks more at the relationship between people and society, for example at whether, as families have changed, parents' attitudes to disciplining children have changed. Social policy specialists try to understand how political and economic forces can be channelled to produce new ways of organising society. As a result, it is very easy for 'experts' from the different disciplines to talk *past* rather than *to* each other.

A practitioner like Bernice has to learn to live with these differences and take what seems to be most relevant from each discipline. But sometimes a choice has to be made to give one set of ideas priority over another. For example, you might be convinced by the psychologists' evidence that physical punishment works, but nevertheless decide that it is too risky to allow because of the sociologists' evidence of its association with violence in later life. The different social sciences will keep coming up with evidence, but it is up to the rest of society to decide whether they are asking the right questions.

Where does this leave Bernice in her deliberations about Sue and her daughter? She still didn't feel 100 per cent sure of her position but she had taken a number of ideas from the reading. First, she was persuaded by Straus that there may be long-term effects from physical punishment and this made her feel more sure that she should take some action. From Larzelere and Rosemond one of the important things she picked up was that Sue is inconsistent in her discipline; she isn't using it to make a point or following through a smack with an explanation or a new activity, so it is largely ineffective as well as potentially damaging. Overall, this suggests that some intervention might be desirable. But she is still unsure about the moral issues: should she intervene between a mother and a child, or should she keep her nose out of other people's business?

Key points

- Smacking is associated with risk of psychological problems in adulthood.

- However, a correlation does not prove that one factor caused another.

- Inconsistent discipline may be as damaging as too harsh discipline.

- Evidence can be gathered scientifically but decisions have to be made and prioritised through moral and political debate.

- Deciding whether to intervene will also depend on views about society, families and individual rights.

3.3 Some missing links

Punishment can become sexualised

While Bernice was rummaging through the last week's newspapers she came upon a somewhat humorous article by Barbara Ehrenreich called 'Getting to the bottom of naughtiness' which linked spanking with sex and which shed light on the discomfort Pat expressed about the punishment she had received at her father's hands.

Activity 11 **Spanking and sex**

Allow about 20 minutes Read 'Getting to the bottom of naughtiness' on page 94 now. Make some notes on the connections the author makes between spanking and sex.

Comment The article hints at the sexualisation of punishment, something which the British have a reputation for abroad ... (*le vice anglais*).

There is a connection between spanking and erotica.

There are double standards: people who condemn pornography in public are also willing to stand up for physical punishment of children and wrong-doers.

Ehrenreich takes a fairly relaxed view of what adults do to each other but concludes her article by challenging those who insist on their right to spank the 'under-aged and non-consenting'. In doing so she anticipates one of the key issues we will be looking at later in this unit in terms of the definition of sexual abuse.

This is not one of the issues explored in the spanking debate discussed above, or in the mainstream agenda on children and punishment. Why is this? I came up with two responses.

1   What research can handle

My first response is that it is very difficult to carry out systematic research into the links between sex and punishment. What would count as 'evidence' that a person derived sexual pleasure from spanking? It isn't the sort of thing many parents would readily admit to in an interview or even an anonymous questionnaire. And the children would not necessarily be reliable witnesses, either at the time or in later years. What is more, the whole notion runs so contrary to popular ideas about families and parenthood that a researcher might run into a lot of resistance and aggression. It would take a subtle and painstaking line of enquiry to make progress in an area like this.

Ehrenreich's arguments are based on such cases as the Internet web site. But this might have been set up by one crank and be accessed by very few people. A social science researcher would not know what confidence to place in this kind of one-off 'evidence' and would tend to ignore it. The same applies to the personal experience and anecdotes that Ehrenreich draws in. They have not been gathered systematically enough to find their way into a scientific report. Although anecdotes are often the way that people who are powerless get their stories on to the official agenda, such evidence tends to be filtered out of scientific discourses.

Getting to the bottom of naughtiness

Barbara Ehrenreich

Maybe it all started with those voluptuous images of young Michael Fay facing down a Singaporean spanking squad, because suddenly there's a rush to paddle the bottoms of America's youth. Prodded by the Christian right, with its militant concept of 'parental rights', school districts all over the country are debating bringing back the paddle, and a bill before the New Hampshire legislature would subject teenage graffiti vandals to public bare-bottom spankings – administered, no doubt, by the legislators themselves.

Spanking advocates like California Assemblyman Mickey Conroy laugh off 'ivory towers' studies showing that corporal punishment only deepens the incorrigibility of the young – after all, he was paddled as a boy himself and look how he turned out. Conroy, who keeps a collection of paddles in his office and enjoys carrying one around, seems to have grasped one of the more bizarre themes from the sexual underground: that whatever else it is – 19th-century nastiness or enlightened tough love – spanking can be fun!

What to do when confronted with another trend straight from the dark recesses of the Republican id? One goes to the source: in this case, to venues such as the urban weeklies' 'Anything Goes' personal ads or the Internet's alt.sex.spanking news group, which are chock full of invitations to party with paddles and pants down. Our pro-spanking guardians of law and order should find plenty of kindred spirits in ads such as 'Good looking white male, prof, early 40s, looking for naughty girl in need of firm, bare-bottomed OTK [Over The Knee]'. Or maybe they'd want to contact the 'Naughty boy' who feels his transgressions have earned him a 'bare-butt spanking, hard!'.

The Christian right, which has otherwise done so little to open up the frontiers of human sexual experience, has been campaigning vigorously for the corporal punishment of children for well over a decade. One of their flagship groups, Focus on the Family, advocates it as a means of safeguarding 'family values', and the right's original Family Protect Act, first floated in 1980, would have prohibited any federal attempt to outlaw spanking or strengthen the statutes against child abuse. So at last we know what it is they like so much about 'the family': where else, except in a Calvin Klein ad, will you find a group of nubile young people whose every gesture and sneer seems to cry out for a little OTK?

No doubt the pro-spanking fellows would insist that their interest in paddling is purely asexual, and that the depraved practices of consenting adults have nothing to do with the loving correction of bad little children. But as the spanking personals make all too clear, the adult practice of 'erotic spanking' derives its erotic charge entirely from fantasies of kinky incest. In alt.sex.spanking, for example, stern 'dads' routinely advertise for 'naughty' spankees, or offer to share their family fun, as in 'My teenaged step-daughter has been bad again. I had to put her over my knee to warm her butt. Turned out it warmed us both up! ... Pictures and audio available.'

Perhaps you think this sort of stuff doesn't belong in a family newspaper – but then what is it doing in a 'pro-family' agenda? If a neighbour starts ranting about bare buttocks or the efficacy of various paddling devices, you'd probably keep the kids locked indoors. But if he does the same thing in a legislative chamber, there's a heartfelt applause for his commitment to 'old-fashioned values'.

Far be it from me to condemn anyone's erotic proclivities, but surely nothing would be lost by getting the spanking freaks out of the legislatures and into the 'adult' milieus that specialise in their peculiar tastes. Let the spanking advocates of the political right take a tip from savvy recreational spankers, and seek out the potential spankees on alt.sex.spanking or thereabouts. As for those who continue to insist on their right to spank the under-aged and non-consenting: the challenge will be to come up with some form of punishment, preferably administered by bands of teenage vigilantes, that these miscreants will not enjoy.

(*Guardian*, 17 May 1996, p. 21)

2   Gender differences in attitudes to punishment

My second observation is about the gender and vested interests of the people who control the debate. The debate you analysed was conducted solely by men. It is interesting that the 'experts' on punishment happen to be men when most childrearing in Western societies is done by women. You saw something similar in Unit 1, where it was pointed out that the theory of maternal deprivation was developed by a man, John Bowlby, and that many of the expert voices telling women how to be good mothers were also male.

One in-depth research study which sheds some light on the gender issues at the heart of the punishment debate was conducted by Angus (1988). In a book on Catholic schooling in Australia he refers to physical violence as 'the steel that reinforces the cement of masculine culture' (p. 103) and recounts an incident in which boys from years seven and eight were strapped in front of their classmates in an assembly. In one school he was studying such 'displays of physical violence' were infrequent, but 'performed in public with the rituals of theatre [so that] the impact on pupils is maximised' (p. 103). Attitudes among the other teachers varied but most disapproval came from the few women teachers of the boys in this age group. Their disapproval, he reports, was not so much about the rights and wrongs of the punishment itself but at 'being asked to leave the scene of public humiliation before the strapping could proceed'. The women teachers felt their authority was greatly undermined by such polarisation and by the reliance of male teachers on the use of physical punishment which was not something they could fall back on. The author suggests that the presence of women teachers has implicitly challenged the pre-eminence of physical modes of control and discipline and, as you can see from the cuttings overleaf, attitudes have changed significantly about this issue.

Key points

- Corporal punishment features heavily in pornography and smacking or caning can become sexualised. This is rarely addressed openly in the debates about punishment or discipline.

- The reasons for the omission of this aspect of the debate are connected to the difficulty of conducting reliable research on the matter and the relative power of men to set the terms of public debate.

The voice of children

Not only are women less prominent in the debate but so are children, the recipients of discipline – I have not quoted any consumer surveys or

customer satisfaction data about the issue! When people tell you 'it did me no harm' they are usually adults looking back. It is difficult to get an objective view from children about punishment they have been on the receiving end of. If we have been punished by parents who we believe love us, how can we reconcile this with rejecting their actions?

Alice Miller, a prominent German psychoanalyst, has written a great deal about childrearing, partly because of her belief that enforced 'obedience' in childrearing techniques in pre-war Germany contributed to the culture which gave rise to the Nazi regime. She

Christian Brothers' head apologises for past abuse

David Sharrock Ireland Correspondent

The leader of an Irish religious teaching order yesterday became the latest Catholic functionary to apologise for any physical and sexual abuse its members may have inflicted.

Brother Edmund Garvey, the congressional leader of the Christian Brothers, a teaching order of professed celibates who do not have the rank of priesthood, made the apology while being made a freeman of his home town of Drogheda, County Louth.

He told the ceremony: 'People have had negative experiences with the Christian Brothers and schools in the past. I cannot deny that, nor do I want to.

'For those who did have hurtful experiences I apologise and ask forgiveness. All I can do is ask for forgiveness.'

The Christian Brothers, whose founder, Edmund Ignatius Rice, was beatified last year, are the latest in a line of Irish Catholic organisations to admit wrongdoing.

The Catholic hierarchy's retreat was first signalled by the news four years ago that the Bishop of Galway, Eamon Casey, had a teenage son. Since then the church has been besieged with allegations that it has attempted to cover up incidents of sex abuse by its priests, as well as claims that nuns brutalised their orphan charges.

On RTE radio yesterday, Brother Garvey made it clear his apology specifically related to such charges. 'I don't want any ambiguity to be around in the minds of people who have been hurt or damaged by anything that has been done in the past,' he said.

'I will not deny it, I cannot deny it, and I will not try to deny it. But I need to ask for forgiveness.'

Brother Garvey told RTE he was talking about and dealing with those occasions 'in which

'For those who did have hurtful experiences I apologise. All I can do is ask for forgiveness.' Edmund Garvey

'The brothers were very tough and almost every day we were all beaten fairly hard. I dreaded school.' Gay Byrne

we are clearly exposed in the media for having excessively physically abused, and sometimes even sexually abused children in our care.

'Obviously, I cannot accept every allegation that is reported or made. But I do believe every allegation has to be fully investigated.'

He highlighted 'harshness, difficulty, at times cruelty' that had been experienced by men, women and children. 'I am sorry to say that at times, with some of our men, we reflected some of that harshness and cruelty only too adequately. I believe all I can do is ask for forgiveness.'

Stories of the brutality of the brothers' schools are legion and have left their mark on generations of Irishmen, many of whom remember the anti-British ethos their teachers strived to inculcate. Every Fianna Fail prime minister from Eamon de Valera to Albert Reynolds has been a Christian Brothers pupil.

Gay Byrne, Ireland's most famous media personality, admits his years with the Christian Brothers in Dublin were awful.

'The brothers were very tough and almost every day we were all beaten fairly hard. I dreaded school.'

But Mr Byrne also recognises that for the vast majority of Irish boys there would not have been second level education without them. 'The main objective of the brothers was to get us through our exams and make sure that we got good jobs in the civil ser-

vice. They worked in appalling circumstances.'

Gerry Adams, the Sinn Fein president, also attended a brothers school in Belfast, as did his colleague, Martin McGuinness, in Derry.

Edmund Ignatius Rice, a Waterford merchant, founded the brothers in 1802. The organisation was credited with helping to build the foundations of the Irish educational system. After independence, it was one of the religious forces to which successive governments abdicated the responsibility of providing education, leaving it in the hands of the clergy, a notoriously repressive force.

The brothers style of education was frequently heavily imbued with republicanism. They are now a dwindling band of fewer than 600 middle-aged and elderly brothers. Over a six-year period they have had only one recruit.

Last year 5,000 Irish people, including cabinet ministers and senior opposition politicians, attended the beatification ceremony in Rome of Edmund Rice, the major step towards being declared a saint. People have been collecting testimonies for his beatification since 1911, and his 'cause' was officially launched in 1961. In 1993 Pope John Paul II declared him 'venerable' and he now requires only one more miracle through intercessions before canonisation.

(Guardian, 16 April 1997)

I was not unruly or slow. I was just an average punching bag for a band of unpolished pedagogues

Peter Lennon on his punishing schooldays

Every day I came home from school my parents would ask: 'How many biffs did you get today?'

It was the 1940s and I was going to one of the most celebrated Christian Brothers' schools in Ireland, Dublin's Synge Street. I was not an unruly pupil, nor was I slow to learn. I was just your average punching bag for Edmund Ignatius Rice's band of unpolished pedagogues.

Physical collision was their preferred method of terrifying knowledge into you. The entire nation accepted this behaviour and when it occasionally got out of hand the explanation was that the poor men (not the unfortunate victim) 'didn't have the consolation of the Mass' and they were exonerated.

People were more discreet about the fact that neither did they have the consolation of a concubine.

I got a hot tip on my first day: a kid told me to learn how to spell 'ecclesiastical' and I'd be well in. Despite the fright of a first public performance I stood up and spelt out eccleesiastical (getting only three biffs) and I have never had trouble with the word since.

The routine instrument of punishment was 'the leather', a stocky object about eight inches long, made of four or five layers of tightly stitched leathers. When it became flabby through use they would stitch in coins to harden the tip.

You would stand out in front

Tapestry of Edmund Ignatius Rice at St Peter's Basilica in Rome during his beatification

of the class, the brother swinging his fist high, skirts and sleeves flying like Mandrake the Magician. Then you had a sensation on your palm of being stung by a dozen bees.

More dreaded was the pointer. A long polished wooden stick, thick at one end, pointed at the other, this would be brought down on your fingers with a crack that shot agony from skull to heel.

When you were not being beaten you witnessed ritual beatings. For some time I was in a room with three classes of 30 pupils each. The beatings went on from the age of about seven to 13. The reason it stopped at 13 was tactical: by 14, boys were big, broad, muscular and bolshie, and stories of a heroic adolescent finally flooring a Christian Brother were undoubtedly behind the sudden man-to-man relationship in senior school.

At day school, there were no instances of serious sexual abuse, but some teachers were known 'messers'. One came a cropper publicly.

He was one of those ingratiating creatures with an oily benevolence who liked to make boys who did not know their lessons stand with him at his desk and, cooing reproaches, would put his hand up your short trousers.

One day he chose the wrong boy. A big lad, redoing his year for about the third time, he was a bit of a simpleton. Standing half hidden by the desk beside the stooping, fawning brother he suddenly roared out: 'Jaysus, he's got me be the bollicks.'

The unfortunate man had a nervous breakdown. I can't say I wish for Edmund Ignatius Rice's band of terrorists a fate worse than that which, by now, has no doubt befallen many of them: oblivion.

(*Guardian*, 16 April 1997)

uses the concept of 'idealisation' to explain how it is that children often do not remember or blame their parents for hurting them. They would rather accept that they 'deserved' any punishment, however severe, than lose their ideal of a good and loving parent. She argues that:

> *The child's dependence on his or her parents' love ... makes it impossible in later years to recognise these traumatizations, which often remain hidden behind the early idealization of the parents for the rest of the child's life.*
>
> *Miller, 1987, p. 4)*

In her work she tries to count the costs of severe punishment in emotional rather than behavioural terms. She writes:

> *An enormous amount can be done to a child in the first few years: he or she can be moulded, dominated, taught good habits, scolded and punished – without any repercussions for the person raising the child and without the child taking revenge ... If he is prevented from reacting in his own way because the parents cannot tolerate his reactions (crying, sadness, rage) ... then the child will learn to be silent. This silence is a sign of the effectiveness of the pedagogical principles applied but at the same time is a danger signal pointing to future pathological development. If there is absolutely no possibility of reacting to hurt, humiliation, and coercion, then these experiences cannot be integrated into the personality: the feelings they evoke are repressed, and the need to articulate them remains unsatisfied, without any hope of being fulfilled. It is this lack of hope of ever being able to express ... relevant feelings that most often causes severe psychological problems.*
>
> *(Miller, 1987, p. 7)*

Her view could be summarised as 'it works but sometimes at a terrible cost'.

According to this view, Sue's daughter may be storing up trouble for the future: we saw that she was not allowed to cry when she was slapped in the supermarket, although this was her first reaction. She is too young not to need her mother's approval, which she seeks by showing her paintings and activities, for example, and she certainly can't challenge her mother's actions. According to Miller, she may well explain the hurt she is experiencing as being her own fault, or a sign that her mother loves her and that 'love equals hurt'. This ties in with Straus's idea of punishment as having a hidden agenda about 'hitting people you love'.

Key points

- Young children are not in a position to question the behaviour of their parents or to express their feelings of rage or humiliation.

- Children may internalise too harsh punishment as being 'deserved'.

3.4 Deciding whether to intervene

Bernice found one more helpful article. It summarises many of the steps we have taken so far in this unit. This time it deals very directly with the issue she was grappling with of whether Sue's parenting had crossed the threshold of seriousness to the extent that intervention was warranted. This paper draws together lessons from a number of recent programmes of research on child protection issues about the problems of definition.

Activity 12   Steps to a decision

Allow about 20 minutes

Read the extract from the Dartington Social Research Unit's *Messages from Research* in the Reader, Chapter 27.

Note down the steps Bernice might work through to reach a decision she feels comfortable with.

Comment   This outline clarifies a number of steps which Bernice went through in making her judgment.

(a)   It asks if there are single, isolated acts which could be said to be abusive but concludes that many happen in ordinary, non-abusive households too, so ...

(b)   It sets up the idea of a 'threshold' within which an act is placed:
- on a continuum and
- in a context.

(c)   It asks what harm may come of the action in the long term and sets out the consequences of 'low warmth, high criticism' parenting styles, arguing for input which helps to bolster support for families to reverse this.

So what do you think Bernice might decide? The 'low warmth, high criticism' framework seemed to sum up Sue's parenting style and the harm it could do to her daughter. It might also be a partial explanation of the different ways in which Allan and Pat's brother responded to their respective fathers' discipline. Bernice decided to make a formal report to the social worker who liaises with the playgroup within the next few days. Is that what you would have decided?

We have considered the issue of physical abuse in relation to children and we saw that in order to make a judgment we had to do far more than say 'hitting is wrong'. We had to look at what kind of hitting, how hard and in what context it took place; whether there were positive reasons for it and/or what damage it might do. We have also spent time considering 'society's' views about children, discipline and punishment. We make decisions within all these reference points – Bernice for example accepts the arguments for limited discipline and feels comfortable with the way her parents brought her and Allan up, where any punishment was counterbalanced by a lot of encouragement and support. It is the absence of these positive emotional qualities as much as the presence of the physical punishment which led her to decide to intervene in relation to Sue. By reporting the incident to social services, who carry the official mandate for 'child protection', Bernice moved this relationship into the public arena to be scrutinised by professionals.

Key points

- While smacking children is very common, it may still be harmful.

- The debate about punishment tends to switch between considering whether or not it works and whether or not it is 'right': these are separate questions.

- Scientists can test the questions asked but choosing and prioritising the questions may be as significant as finding answers.

- Physical punishment is a risk factor for psychological problems in the long term.

- A low warmth, high criticism style of parenting is considered to be the worst of both worlds for a young child.

3.5 What about the grown ups?

We have considered the rights and wrongs of hitting children at length but Sue's daughter is not the only person who has been hit in the last two weeks. Allan was hit by the man outside the pub. What Pat did not know was that:

- Pat's mother has been hit by her father who got frustrated by her wetting the bed

- Jesse (Pat and Allan's son) has been hit by a school bully

- Sue has been hit by her boyfriend.

How are these incidents 'constructed' and what responsibility do we have as workers or as citizens if we 'know' about or anticipate such violence? Does 'society' have any right to get involved in these other situations at all or is the relationship between parents and children a special case? The Dartington Report acknowledges that:

> *Society continually reconstructs definitions of maltreatment which sanction intervention ... The State remains selective in its concerns and there is a difference between behaviour known to be harmful to children and behaviour which attracts the attention of child protection practitioners. For example, professionals' interest in school bullying is not as great as parents and children would wish it to be and domestic violence is only just beginning to achieve salience as a cause of concern.*
>
> *(Dartington Social Research Unit, 1995, p. 15)*

The state is selective not only in relation to children but also when it comes to violence directed against adults. In these instances of physical violence, the incident involving Allan was the only one where the police were involved. Why? Is it because:

- it occurred in public
- they are not members of the same family
- they are both men?

If you compare this with Sue's situation, you can see that all three factors were absent, which could explain the lack of any public intervention.

- Sue's partner hit her in the privacy of their own home, not in public.
- Sue and her partner can be seen as part of one nuclear family.
- Sue is a woman, her partner is male.

On the other hand, Pat's mum was also hit in private, by a member of her family, and by a man – but there is a difference. She is an older person in receipt of limited community care services (she has several hours of domiciliary care a week), and would fall within the remit of her local social services adult protection policy because she qualifies as a vulnerable adult, defined in new legislation proposed by the Law Commission as:

> *... any person of 18 or over who is, or may be, in need of Community Care services by reason of mental, or other, disability, age or illness and who is, or may be, unable to take care of himself or herself or unable to protect himself or herself against significant harm or serious exploitation.*
>
> *(Law Commission, 1995, p. 207)*

 This proposed legislation introduces the notion of significant harm as a measure of vulnerability and a signal for outside intervention and, if enacted, will bring adult protection in line with the principles of the Children Act 1989.

We noted in Block 1 how care in families becomes an issue worthy of public attention when it is exceptional. Here is another instance where family life is potentially open to public scrutiny and regulation because Pat's mother has care needs over and above the norm. But this does not mean that her situation will necessarily come to light. Pat's mother would consider it disloyal to mention such a thing to an outsider. She doesn't even tell her daughter in case it worries her.

Sue, on the other hand, will not be covered by the adult protection policy. She is afraid she will get hurt and feels hopeless because she has nowhere to go. These examples show that being acknowledged as someone deserving of protection is something of a lottery if you are

Would you want to be called a 'vulnerable adult'?

being abused within the home/family or within residential care. Just as a degree of physical violence is thought to be legitimate between parents and children if it is construed as discipline or punishment, so an element of control is often accepted, and even approved of, in relationships between men and women, or between carer and cared for.

Some of the confusion of moral values on these matters in society at large is reflected in popular culture – music, drama, newspapers, TV, cinema. I have selected four songs to illustrate how violence between men and women merges into accepted images of romantic and marital relationships and how this ideology is internalised by women. The songs span a 30-year period.

Activity 13   Domestic violence in popular culture

Allow about 15 minutes   Listen to Audio Cassette 6, side 1, part 3 and look at the Media Notes. On
      it are four songs:

(a)   Louis Jordan, 'Gal, you need a whipping', 1954

(b)   The Crystals, 'He hit me (it felt like a kiss)', 1962

(c)   Sandy Posey, 'Born a woman', 1966

(d)   The Police, 'Every breath you take', 1983.

Note down how the themes of each song indicate a cultural acceptance of violent behaviour in male–female relationships.

Comment   The first song, 'Gal, you need a whipping', rehearses the notion, prevalent in both white and black communities, that men are entitled to a 'service' from women and to apply sanctions if they do not come up to scratch. This song illustrates graphically the confusion between love and control, sex and punishment.

The second song, 'He hit me (it felt like a kiss)', reinforces this notion and shows how these attitudes persisted into the so-called permissive 1960s. The title encapsulates the way violence can be redefined as an act of love and is all the more powerful because it is sung by women, for women.

Goodbye to bliss

Hard to believe, but pregnancy can mean the start of domestic violence.

In romantic films, an expectant mother can expect flowers, chocolates and congratulations from her delighted husband. It's such a seductive stereotype that even those who should know better, such as midwives and gynaecologists, cling to it. Yet research suggests that pregnancy may trigger domestic violence rather than domestic bliss. Studies in the US and Canada show that up to 21 per cent of pregnant women have been abused by their partners, with many of the women first experiencing violence during pregnancy.

(*Guardian*, 11 June 1997)

Sign of the crimes

For the first time, UNICEF has included in its annual Progress of the Nations report a specific section on violence against women.

... The feminist rhetoric being used is staggeringly bold. There is a new category, 'gender crime', bringing together practices such as bride burning, dowry crimes, domestic beatings and genital mutilation which have recently been examined in isolation. The change is particularly significant because no one seems to be worrying any more about accusations of cultural imperialism. Previously, the fear of judging other cultures sometimes halted feminist criticism of attacks on women in other countries.

(*Guardian*, 24 July 1997)

The third song shows how individual women internalise this ideology of control until what exists in the outside world as a set of values forged out of unequal power relations becomes wrapped up as a 'natural' part of 'being a woman'.

The last song, 'Every breath you take', also reinforces the idea of ownership ('you belong to me', 'I'll be watching you' ...), a construct which is borne out by the fact that individual women are most at risk of life-threatening violence when they attempt to leave or have recently left a violent partner (see Holder *et al.*, 1994, p. 5). The song shows what a fine line there is between the two sides of romantic ideology – presented as being about love it can easily tip over into control and threat.

The hierarchical relationship which underlies these songs is one which is referred to by feminists as 'patriarchal' and is strongly supported within major world religions: it provides a structure and order but at the cost of suppressing women's interests within the private and public spheres. Some theorists see sexist oppression as a mirror of, or compensation for, the economic oppression which men were/are subjected to in their working lives. Even though these lyrics might seem rather extreme, these attitudes remain very central to our culture and institutions and can become ingrained in the way individuals fantasise about and conduct their relationships.

Many police forces are now seeking to reverse the practice of treating domestic violence as a *private* matter and are developing closer links with other agencies and services. This will be discussed in more detail in the next unit.

Should we tolerate any violence in personal relationships?

Key points

- Violence between adults is treated arbitrarily depending on the gender (and often race) of the victim.

- Some degree of violence towards women is often condoned within marital and sexual relationships.

- Vulnerable people often have no way of telling anyone what is happening to them.

- Some individuals, like Sue, are both victim and perpetrator and need support and intervention in both cases.

Section 4
Sexual abuse

In Section 3 we worked through the process of evaluating *physical* abuse as it relates to children and briefly considered some of the anomalies which occur when considering such abuse towards adults. We started by examining the popular consensus around limited smacking of children as part of normal discipline which makes the issues of context crucial in deciding where the dividing line should be. We saw that a single incident would probably not be enough to warrant intervention under child protection procedures even if it were quite severe. Do the same considerations come into play when it is *sexual*, rather than physical, abuse at issue? In the extract from *Messages from Research* which you read in Section 3, a number of differences are suggested:

- Whereas for other forms of abuse a single event would probably not be enough to trigger intervention, in relation to sexual abuse even a relatively minor incident may require immediate and definite action.

- The thresholds which define a sexual act are more clear-cut: there is less of a continuum and much more agreement about what constitutes a sexually abusive act.

- Sexual abuse of children is less context specific: it cannot be justified and there are no extenuating circumstances which excuse abuse within family relationships.

Sexual abuse is also more likely to be a serial and repeated form of behaviour by abusers, leading to ongoing risk to other children or vulnerable adults if no action is taken. It is not situational; that is, it is not brought on by a particular set of circumstances. Evidence from abusers suggests that they actively set up the circumstances and relationships within which they abuse by targeting suitably vulnerable children or adults and working their way into positions of trust (see for example Waterhouse *et al.*, 1994).

Where there is support for some physical discipline there is an equally vehement outcry against any sexual abuse of children, and increasingly against the sexual abuse of vulnerable adults. But we have seen in relation to physical assaults that it makes a difference who the victim is, whether they are seen as blameless and worth protecting and whether they can access anyone to whom they can disclose what is happening. We will see that this is equally true of sexual abuse and that there are certain blind spots which allow some children and adults to be taken advantage of.

Key points

- There is more consensus about the threshold at which sexual acts committed against children are deemed to be abuse and to trigger intervention.

- Even a single act might lead to decisive action being taken.

- Sexual abusing tends to be repeated by perpetrators and often involves deliberate and planned targeting of children or vulnerable adults.

4.1 The centrality of consent

In this section we will briefly look at what makes a sexual act abusive and unpack this to include a more detailed consideration of capacity and consent. After all, people often want to have sex with each other and sex with someone you want to have sex with is prized within Western societies. So consent is a critical defining issue and adds an extra step into the process of definition which we worked through in relation to physical abuse. Consent may cut across the evaluation of the actual act or damage which has been done. For example, at the time of writing the celebrated 'Spanner' case was being referred to the European Court of Human Rights for appeal. This case centred on a group of gay men who had been convicted for engaging in consenting sado-masochistic acts. The acts themselves were very damaging and serious and the state argued that they were inherently indecent, but the men's defence was that they had entered into them voluntarily.

In contrast to this, a case in the United States which occurred at about the same time was 'met with horror and incredulity' because it concerned a woman who had been raped and had subsequently become pregnant despite being in a coma. Here there could be no question but that the man convicted had intended to exploit the woman: there were no mitigating factors, he could not argue that she had gone along with it, had given double messages or had in some way contributed by 'asking for it' – arguments which are often made by defence lawyers in criminal rape trials. It was a cut and dried case and what made it so was the very obvious lack of consent on the part of the woman concerned and the extraordinary ethical issues raised by her pregnancy.

Coma rape victim pregnant

Ian Katz in New York

Even in a country accustomed to a daily diet of criminal grotesqueries, the rape of a woman aged 29 who has been in a coma for 10 years has been met with horror and incredulity.

The reaction of the woman's parents has shocked the United States almost as much as the crime itself: they have refused to abort the resulting pregnancy on religious grounds.

The case has sparked a debate among doctors and medical ethicists about what rights can be ascribed to the woman, whose identity has been withheld, the foetus, and the family.

'The woman's body is being used as a vessel, reducing her to more of a thing than a person' bioethicist Ellen Moskowitz told USA Today. 'It could be offensive to her humanity.' If she is permanently unconscious, however, 'the wrong done to her is not profound'.

The attack was discovered in December after nursing staff at the Westfall Health Care Centre in Rochester, New York, noticed a slight swelling of the woman's stomach. Tests quickly showed that she was four to five-and-a-half months pregnant.

The woman's family was told that if the pregnancy was not terminated, she should have given birth in May. Her parents said they would not sanction an abortion because of their religious beliefs, and because they wanted a reminder of their daughter. Though there is no record of a comatose woman becoming pregnant, there have been numerous cases of patients giving birth while in a coma.

The pregnant woman was a devout Catholic, and friends say she strongly opposed abortion. She had just been accepted for the prestigious Cornell College when she was injured in a car crash at the age of 19.

She has remained in a coma ever since, breathing without assistance but fed by a tube.

No one has been arrested in connection with the rape, believed to have taken place in August. A former aide who worked at the centre at the time was charged in November with sexually abusing a disabled patient aged 49.

(*Guardian*, 31 January 1996, p. 1)

These issues are spelt out in the next Offprint article you will be reading, which focuses on consent issues in the context of sexual abuse of adults with learning difficulties. The paper starts by setting out the same kind of continuum which we sketched out in relation to physical abuse, with sexual acts put on a scale from teasing and innuendo (non-contact abuse) through to touch, masturbation and penetrative sex (contact abuse). But as we saw earlier in the unit, such a classification is not in itself a sufficient indicator of the seriousness of any incident. The paper introduces factors which have been highlighted in relation to child sexual abuse around power, authority and dependence, and translates these into the situations in which adults with learning difficulties find themselves. It then goes into more detail about what valid consent means, dealing separately with whether the person has given consent, their capacity to consent, and 'barriers' and inequality in the form of authority, force or pressure which undermine their ability to freely consent.

Activity 14   Sexual abuse and adults with learning difficulties

Allow about 30 minutes   Read Offprint 33.

When you have read it, listen to Betty Fisher, who speaks on side 2 of Audio Cassette 6. She describes how her son was sexually abused by a member of his church.

(a)   Listen to what she has to say and decide for yourself whether you consider this to have been abuse. Use the framework summarised in Table 2 of Offprint 33. Did Garry consent, could he consent, did the man exert undue force or control over him?

(b)   How serious do you consider this abuse to have been? Look back to the criteria of seriousness in Section 2.3 and use these as a reference point. On a scale of 1–10 (where 10 is the most serious) where would you place this incident?

(c)   How could this incident have been prevented?

(d)   In what ways did the legal process create barriers to Garry's receiving justice?

Comment   (a)   Yes, this does seem to have been abuse. It was perpetrated within an ongoing relationship between people of unequal power. The perpetrator intended to take advantage of Garry, who:
- did not consent to the sexual contact
- probably lacked the capacity to consent, and
- was both tricked into it and then forced to endure it.

Any one of these would have been enough to define this act as non-consenting and abusive. Although the man was not a member of staff, he had 'authority' as a member of the church, which he used to get access to Garry and to avoid questions about his intentions or behaviour.

(b)   I would place this incident at the more serious end of the scale. The incident has had a lasting impact on Garry's mental health and has caused great distress to his family. The man seemed to have deliberately targeted Garry as a vulnerable person and, given what we know about the serial nature of sexual offending, is likely to gravitate towards abusing other vulnerable adults unless he is stopped. On a scale of 1–10 I would probably place it at about 8. What did you think?

(c) Betty queried why the service had not checked up on the man, where he lived, how suitable and accessible this would be for Garry, or what the arrangements would be for Garry's stay. She says they were 'naive'. They assumed everything would be OK because the man was a member of the church. Although it is not normal to have friends vetted, in this case it might have prevented considerable distress.

(d) The court proceedings were not helpful to Garry. In court Garry was asked inappropriate 'double negative' questions, he was asked to take the oath, and he had to come face to face with his abuser without a screen or video loop being made available. Betty says there was no attempt to 'establish a relationship' with him as a person with learning difficulties who was acting as a witness in court. This lack of attention to the special needs of people with learning difficulties is a barrier to their receiving justice.

Justice for all?

Consent is a complex issue and one where unstated assumptions often confuse judgments. It is often thought that a woman who has been out for dinner with a man has consented to sex, or that her consent on one occasion implies her consent at all times, and these attitudes permeate the legal system (Lees, 1996). A woman's right to withhold her consent to sex within marriage has only recently been conceded. Women's testimony is sometimes undermined as irrational or malicious. These problems in guaranteeing personal autonomy in sexual encounters affect *all* women. As Doyal says, 'women have often lacked the social or economic autonomy to underpin sexual choices' (1995, p. 60). Even in marriage their consent may be co-opted as a part of the economic and personal service bargain. For some, the issues are even more complex and difficult. The issue, as we saw in the offprint, is not only whether the person gave consent on a particular occasion but whether they were able to make that judgment, in other words whether they had the 'capacity' to make that decision. We considered capacity as an issue in relation to Tony and the discussion about whether he should be tagged. It comes up again as a complex issue in relation to sex – this is something which someone else can't decide on your behalf in a case conference, so what happens if you can't decide for yourself?

Consider these three examples:

1   Pat's mother increasingly demonstrates symptoms of dementia and is losing her capacity to make decisions for herself but her husband still wants and expects to have sex with her. At what point does this become an infringement of her rights? How is anyone likely to find out if Pat's mother dislikes the sex or wants it to stop: she may well not say anything or communicate her distress about so personal a matter. If Pat were aware of this side of her parents' relationship, should she intervene, and if so how?

2   A woman cited in Brown and Keating (in press) had been admitted to a psychiatric hospital under a section and while in hospital she entered, seemingly willingly, into a sexual relationship with a fellow patient. Afterwards she argued that the hospital staff should have prevented her from doing so because she had lacked capacity. She claimed that this was not a relationship she would have entered into if she had been well.

3   The girlfriend of Pat's cousin Derek is a young woman with severe learning difficulties and although she likes Derek and enjoys the status of 'having a boyfriend' she does not really understand what sex involves or any of the risks which go with it. According to the law (Sexual Offences Act 1956) she is deemed unable to give her consent because of the level of her learning disability. Derek might be able to argue that he did not appreciate her inability to give consent and this would be a defence in the unlikely event that their relationship were ever to lead to a court case: it is much more likely that it would be left to the staff of the service or professionals to make a judgment about whether the relationship should be allowed to continue, a point that was made in Unit 22.

In these three examples the central issue is capacity to consent, but the issues surrounding it and the subsequent problems in assessment and intervention are very different. While Pat's mother is losing her capacity to consent, the woman with mental health problems has fluctuating capacity to make her own decisions and it is possible that Derek's girlfriend is never going to be able to exercise capacity in relation to sexual relationships.

Meanwhile, as we saw for Garry, a further issue is not only whether someone can and does give their consent, but the context within which they do so. Many people at some time in their lives have sexual relationships in which they may be left feeling exploited or deceived. At what point does this invalidate their consent? Clearly, if you have consented to something at knife point you have not consented freely, but what if you believed your partner loved you, or might marry you, and you later found out (s)he didn't? Does that level of deception cut across or invalidate your 'informed' consent? Moreover, there may be situations in which one person doesn't have to use force, but can draw on the persuasive power of the pinstripe or the credit card and effectively buy consent. At an individual level this might look like, and be defended as, individual choice, but when it adds up it can be seen that inequality substantially disadvantages many people in their sexual lives. Perhaps the material basis of what looks like a freely entered into sexual transaction is most clear in relation to prostitution, but poverty is the bottom line which effectively shapes and limits many people's sexual options and relationships. Kelly *et al.* (1995) argue, 'the sex industry relies upon, and trades in, all forms of inequality' (p. 12). It also confuses issues of responsibility and blame. I started out by asserting that there is almost universal condemnation of sexual abuse against children, but if that were so how could it be that until 1997 when girls under 16 were involved in prostitution it was they, and not their punters, who were cautioned, 'for what in effect, and in law, is an offence against them' (Kelly *et al.*, 1995, p. 31)?

Translated on to a global level, we see inequality between countries fuelling a trade in 'sex tourism'. Issues of geography, race, gender and age are transcended by the argument that:

> *The majority of children in the world who are victims of sexual exploitation come from poor, often but not exclusively Black, countries. What connects these children with children abused from rich western countries is that they are trying to find ways to ensure their own physical survival. Children and young people in desperate circumstances, like many women, learn fairly quickly that if they have nothing else to sell they can sell their bodies ...*

> (*Kelly* et al., 1995, p. 12)

If you think about what makes a 'good' victim it is anyone who is marginalised, unsupported, isolated and not likely to be believed. An abuser would hardly need to use force to abuse such a person.

Key points

In assessing consent there are several considerations:

- whether consent has been given at all

- whether an individual has the capacity to consent at this time

- whether inequality, violence or exploitation negates a child's or adult's consent and 'choice' in sexual matters

- in extreme forms this inequality may boil down to the child's or adult's need for physical survival.

Conclusion

The core questions for Unit 23 were:

How is 'abuse' defined?

- There is no such thing as an objective definition of abuse. The line between abuse and ordinary behaviour is constantly being redrawn. Actions are interpreted in a different light as new issues are brought under the spotlight of research and debate, and new information shapes perceptions. This does not mean that abuse is not real. It means that our acknowledgement of abuse depends on who has the power to challenge the way they are treated, or is seen by others as deserving of protection.

- In this and the previous unit we have seen that there are different responses to personal or sexual violence depending on who is involved and how the relationship is interpreted.

What are the different legal and professional contexts for child and adult protection?

- There is more consensus when abuse occurs in relation to children than there is in relation to adults.

- The legal and professional frameworks within which action can be taken are clearer for children than for vulnerable adults.

- However, as our worked example of corporal punishment of children by their parents showed, there is a great deal of ambiguity when it comes to drawing the line between discipline and abuse.

What criteria can be used for judging the seriousness of different kinds of abuse and abusing?

- The criteria for deciding on seriousness include: the victim's consent; their capacity to consent; the misuse of power by someone in authority; the impact on the person abused, and others; the level of deliberate intention exercised by the abuser; whether the act is against the law; and the likelihood of the abuser repeating the abuse.

Why does abuse happen and what pressures can lead to abusive behaviour?

- Abuse most often happens in circumstances of inequality, including inequalities of age, sex, economic and social power.

- Cultural beliefs also make abuse more of a possibility. For example, the confusion between love, control and possession reflected in popular culture can serve to make violence in intimate relationships between men and women socially acceptable. In relation to children, beliefs about discipline legitimise behaviour which, if it were between adults, would be considered unlawful and abusive.

What part do gender, race, age and poverty play in the dynamics of abusive relationships?

- As we saw above, the key issue is inequality, which is bolstered by ideologies which assert that unequal power is inevitable and 'natural' by claiming that one race or sex is superior and justified in controlling others.

Thinking about these issues is important because as well as being a student of this course you are probably also a carer, a relative, someone on the receiving end of care, or possibly a victim or survivor of abuse. In any of those roles, you have to be clear about where the threshold lies between legitimate control, physical or sexual contact and abuses of power which can lead to significant harm. Taking action against abuse can be a difficult thing to do, but it helps to have the confidence which comes from knowing that you have reached a thoughtful decision.

In the next unit, where we look at what can be done about abusive practice or relationships, the discussion is taken one step further.

References

Angus, L. (1988) *Continuity and Change in Catholic Schooling*, Falmer Press, Lewes.

Brown, H. and Keating, F. (in press) ' "We're doing it already ..." adult protection in mental health services', *Journal of Psychiatric Nursing.*

Brown, H. and Stein, J. (1998) 'Implementing adult protection policies in Kent and East Sussex', *Journal of Social Policy.*

Dartington Social Research Unit (1995) *Child Protection: Messages From Research*, HMSO, London.

Doyal, L. (1995) *What Makes Women Sick: Gender and the Political Economy of Health*, Macmillan, Basingstoke.

East Sussex Social Services (1996) *Guidelines on the Abuse of Vulnerable Adults*, East Sussex County Council, Lewes.

Eastman, M. (1993) 'Fighting it right', *Community Care*, Vol. 6, No. 5, p. 20.

Farmer, E. and Owen, M. (1995) *Child Protection Practice: Private Risks and Public Remedies – Decision Making, Intervention and Outcome in Child Protection Work*, HMSO, London.

Holder, R., Kelly, L. and Singh, T. (1994) *Suffering in Silence: Children and Young People who Witness Domestic Violence*, Domestic Violence Unit, Hammersmith and Fulham.

Kelly, L., Regan, L. and Burton, S. (1991) *An Exploratory Study of the Prevalence of Sexual Abuse in a Sample of 16–21 Year Olds*, Child and Woman Abuse Studies Unit, University of North London.

Kelly, L., Wingfield, R., Burton, S. and Regan, L. (1995) *Splintered Lives: Sexual Exploitation of Children in the Context of Children's Rights and Child Protection*, Barnardo's, Ilford.

Kent County Council Social Services (1995/6) *Child Protection Procedure*, Kent County Council, Maidstone.

Law Commission (1995) *Proposals for a Mental Incapacity Bill*, Cm 235, HMSO, London.

Lees, S. (1996) 'Unreasonable doubt: the outcomes of rape trials' in Hester, M., Kelly, L. and Radford, J. (eds) *Women, Violence and Male Power*, Open University Press, Buckingham, pp. 99–117.

Mason, M. and Gambill, E. (eds) (1994) *Debating Children's Lives*, Sage, Part 3, Debate 12.

Miller, A. (1987) *For Your Own Good: The Roots of Violence in Child Rearing*, Virago Press, London.

Socolar, R. and Stein, R. (1995) 'Spanking infants and toddlers: maternal belief and practice', *Pediatrics*, 1995, pp. 105–11.

Stevenson, O. (1996) *Elder Protection in the Community: What Can We Learn from Child Protection?*, Age Concern Institute of Gerontology, London.

Sundram, C. (1984) 'Obstacles to reducing patient abuse in public institutions', *Hospital and Community Psychiatry*, Vol. 35, No. 3, pp. 238–43.

Waterhouse, L., Dobash, R.P. and Carnie, J. (1994) *Child Sexual Abusers*, The Scottish Office Central Research Unit, Edinburgh.

Williams, C. (1993) 'Vulnerable victims? A current awareness of the victimisation of people with learning disabilities', *Disability, Handicap and Society*, Vol. 8, No. 2, pp. 161–72.

Acknowledgements

Grateful acknowledgement is made to the following sources for permission to reproduce material in this unit:

Text

P. 75: Hunter, L. (1996) 'Are you in an abusive relationship?' *19 Magazine*, 8–13 December 1996, IPC Magazines Ltd with permission from Robert Harding Syndication; p. 80: Thomson, A. (1996) 'Blair admits smacking his children - and feeling remorse', *Times*, 6 June 1996, © Times Newspapers Ltd, 1996; p. 94: Ehrenreich, B. (1996) 'Getting to the bottom of naughtiness', *Guardian*, 17 May 1996, © Guardian Newspapers 1996; p. 96: Sharrock, D. (1997) 'Christian brothers' head apologises for past abuse', *Guardian*, 16 April 1997, © Guardian Newspapers Ltd 1997; p. 97: Lennon, P. (1997) 'I was not unruly or slow. I was just an average punching bag for a band of unpolished pedagogues', *Guardian*, 16 April 1997, © Guardian Newspapers Ltd 1997; p. 105 (centre): Knight, J. 1997, 'Goodbye to bliss', *Guardian*, 11 June 1997, © Guardian Newspapers Ltd 1997; p. 105 (bottom): Coward, R. (1997) 'Sign of the crimes', *Guardian*, 24th July 1997, © Guardian Newspapers Ltd 1997; p. 108: Katz, I. (1996) 'Coma rape victim pregnant', *Guardian*, 31 January 1996, © Guardian Newspapers Ltd 1996.

Figure

P. 71: Brindle, D. (1994) 'Official figures show third of children living in poverty', *Guardian*, 15 July 1994, © Guardian Newspapers 1994.

Table

Table 1: Kettle, M. (1996) 'Parents' role a model for life', *Guardian*, 7 November 1996, © Guardian Newspapers 1996.

Illustrations

Pp. 59 and 95: NSPCC. Photographs posed by models; pp. 70, 73 and 77: NSPCC/Corinne Day.; p. 96 (left): Tom Conachy; p. 96 (right): INPHO Photography; p. 97: PA International; p. 98: Leaflet - Think Before You Smack, courtesy of End Physical Punishment of Children; pp. 102 and 110: Pam Isherwood/Format; p. 103 Jacky Fleming; p. 104: Bryan McAllister; p. 105: Courtesy of Edinburgh District Council Women's Unit, Zero Tolerance Division/Copyright The Estate of Franki Raffles.

Unit 24
Finding Out

Prepared for the course team by Hilary Brown

While you are working on Unit 24, you will need:
- Course Reader
- Offprints Book
- *The Good Study Guide*
- Audio Cassette 6, side 2, part 5
- Care in the UK
- Wallchart

Contents

Introduction

In Units 22 and 23 you looked at the problems of providing personal care in public settings and public scrutiny in personal ones. You saw how confused boundaries could inadvertently lead to abuse, and explored the complicated value judgments involved in deciding when individuals or agencies have overstepped the mark. In this unit the focus is on finding out about abuse and on where to look for reliable information. You will be evaluating knowledge taken from different sources and filtered through different systems and barriers.

Good practice depends on accurate information, but in this field a 'chicken and egg' situation operates, because only where practice is good can information about abuse readily come to light. In the past abuse may not have been recognised, but that does not mean it didn't happen. In Unit 23 we saw how selectively the term is attached to incidents of personal or sexual violence. So it is very difficult to build up information about abuse. A simple counting of cases may not be helpful. If people were not believed when they said they had been abused, or if abuse was considered 'normal' (as with some kinds of corporal punishment and violence in the home), it would not have been recorded. As Stevenson says, 'the whole question of incidence and prevalence is inextricably bound up with social awareness' (1996, p. 4). We might assume that we are in the midst of a great increase in abuse, but, as Overton suggests, what we are actually seeing is a more open and constructive acknowledgement of the issues:

> *Although reported cases of child abuse have risen dramatically in most countries in recent years, there is no evidence to support the idea that we are in the midst of an epidemic of abuse. What we are witnessing is an epidemic of **reporting**. This is surely a good thing. It is revealing a problem which for long was hidden and acknowledging that a problem exists is an essential prerequisite for action to deal with that problem.*
>
> *(1993, p. 75)*

The main goal of this unit is to explore patterns of abuse and their impact on individuals, so that you know what to do if you encounter abusive practice or abusive relationships. Another goal is to think about what kinds of service provision can make a difference. And a parallel goal is to help you *find out* about *finding out* so that you will feel more confident about how to use service evaluations and research studies to inform you about abuse. A word of advice – the readings in this unit come towards the end, so leave time for them.

Core questions

- How can policies and procedures help in abusive situations and relationships?
- What can be learnt from accounts by users, practitioners and whistle-blowers?
- What is the scale of the problem?
- What can we learn from research?
- How can abuse be prevented?
- What do people who have been abused need to help them recover?
- How can appropriate services and interagency partnerships be developed?

Section 1
Developing an adult protection policy

First, we are going to meet up again with Allan, whom we last met when he was recovering from having been punched outside the pub. This is a continuation of the fictional case study which has run through the units in this block. However, the experience of researching these issues in a local authority setting is based closely on a real-life project written up in Brown and Stein (1997). In this study, work was undertaken in two large local authorities to implement policies on abuse of vulnerable adults and to monitor the extent of abuse reported through these policies.

Allan

When Allan returned to work after the broken nose incident he was a bit taken aback to find an urgent memo on his desk from the director, asking him to look into adult abuse ... he hadn't expected to be facing up to this issue again quite so soon! Allan works as an information and planning officer in a local authority social services department. The memo asked him to come to a briefing meeting on his first morning back because the department was to develop an adult abuse policy and the director wanted Allan to do some of the groundwork. The departmental management team wanted some background information on which to base their decisions. They asked Allan to do three things:

- to develop policies and procedures on abuse of vulnerable adults

- report back to the department on the incidence of adult abuse and what the common patterns are

- put forward a plan for service development in partnership with other agencies.

At the meeting, the response from Allan's colleagues was very mixed. Opinion was split: Donald, who was the manager of mental health services, said: 'We are doing all this already ... it is just good social work ... we don't need to call it adult abuse and have loads of forms and registers and a bureaucratic response ... look where it has led in child protection ... you can't sneeze without a dawn raid ...'

On the other hand, Abby, one of the team leaders from the older people's services assessment team, said she thought that care managers tend to turn a blind eye because they *don't know what to do* (she said this emphatically) in these situations. She gave a couple of dreadful examples from her recent caseload: in one an older woman had been beaten by her husband to 'within an inch of her life'; in another a private home care worker had been systematically stealing money from a client, but this had gone unnoticed for years. In both cases there had been early warning signals, which the care managers had ignored or explained away.

Allan's own experience was in working with young people who had been in trouble with the law, and he had dealt with only one serious case of abuse. It occurred shortly after Allan had moved to his previous post with this authority, and involved a volunteer who had been highly thought of by everyone, but who turned out to have sexually abused several young men in the project. The abuse eventually came to light because the police apprehended the man with a rent boy, not because the social services had picked up any of the signals (although, with hindsight, they could see these quite clearly). Allan had been dismayed to find that rumours had been rife for some time, but no one had reported or recorded any concerns which might have alerted him earlier. The young people technically fell within child protection procedures, but these had not been operated with the same level of alertness as they would have been for younger children. He told the meeting about this, and that he could imagine the same thing happening in services for adults with learning difficulties. He said it left him thinking that a formal approach had merits if it would stop hardened abusers getting away with it.

This was countered by Corinne, another manager from older people's services, who said that if the department went down that road it would lead to stressed carers being treated like criminals when all they needed was a bit of respite care.

As the meeting progressed Allan felt that there was quite a lot of confusion: everyone seemed to be talking about something different. The director closed the meeting by muttering that 'we are all on a really sharp learning curve on this issue'. Allan joked to his colleague that his learning curve was going to have to be a vertical line because he didn't know anything about adult abuse at all, at which his friend laughed and said: 'Nonsense, you only got this job because of your first-hand experience! How is your nose coming along?'

When he got back to his office, Allan rang his colleague Dave, who was responsible for handling library-related matters, such as journal requests, for the social services department. Allan wished he hadn't beaten Dave at squash quite so convincingly last time, because he really needed him to pull out the stops now. 'Can't offer a return match just yet', thought Allan, as his nose throbbed and started to bleed slightly. Perhaps Dave would feel sorry for him. Actually, Dave couldn't have been more helpful: he was pleased to have something to get his teeth into. They talked through the issues and he agreed to do a literature search and get copies of some key papers as soon as possible. They agreed to another game but not for a few weeks, and Allan left feeling more cheerful than he had done all day. He thought that his task would prove quite an interesting challenge after all.

1.1   Policies and procedures

Differing interests

Allan's first task was to develop policies and procedures – but what *are* they and *who* are they for? If you work for a social care agency you may have all sorts of booklets and instruction manuals, on anything from administering medication to testing the fire alarm. Each of them will have a different level of importance and status. Some might be compulsory, while others might contain useful information and hints on how to manage difficult situations. Some of the work of a social care agency is set down by law, in which case detailed operational instructions are set out, since the agency has to be able to defend the decisions and interventions of its staff if there is any public disquiet. In these areas, as you saw in Block 5, the freedom of individual staff to act as they think fit is limited, and it will be mandatory for them to report to a senior manager or to write up detailed records.

The impetus for a policy document can come from either care workers or managers, or a combination of both. Care workers may themselves seek guidance and instructions about what they should do in a difficult situation, but managers may also want to impose certain solutions and rule out others. Most policies represent a compromise between this 'bottom-up' pressure for help and a 'top down' concern that practice should adhere to the law, or to agreed principles. Sometimes these two motivations work in harmony, and policies will be welcomed as a useful aid to practice and a useful framework for management. At other times the two 'sides' work against each other: workers may perceive managers to be covering their own backs without offering any useful input or suggestions. A policy may tell you what *not* to do but not how you *should* approach a situation. This can leave workers feeling that they will be blamed if something goes wrong but not helped to get things right (Means and Smith, 1994, p. 43).

The difference between policies and procedures

Generally speaking:

- *policies* state values and broad aims in relation to an area of work; a policy says *what* you are trying to do

- *procedures* set out *how* you are to work in relation to certain issues; a procedure sets down, for example, the way decisions are to be made, by whom and within what time-scale.

In relation to abuse some of this procedural detail will be about who reports *what* to *whom* and *when*, and about the use of case conferences to make decisions in consultation with other agencies. Workers have to follow the spirit (as set out in the policy) and the letter (as set out in the procedures). As Stevenson (1996) says:

> *The issue is one of balance between bureaucratic mechanisms and professional judgments.*
>
> *(p. 17)*

If the balance is achieved, workers will feel that the processes set out in the procedures help them to achieve the aims stated in the policies, while managers will feel that they can keep track of decision making in areas of work that are likely to be the subject of public or political scrutiny.

Allan knew this was going to be a hard balance to achieve. The policy cannot possibly anticipate every eventuality. It has to rely on the judgments of individual workers and make it possible for them to act as they think best, while alerting them to high-risk situations which require more formal input. His own work in the 'twilight zone' between children's and adult services had made him aware of the rather draconian nature of the child protection procedures (captured in the media by stories of 'dawn raids') and the backlash this can set up. In his own local authority a new set of public information leaflets had been issued to try to 'soften' the image of child protection work, so that it is not perceived as a threat. It is counter-productive if people feel they can't ask for help for fear of having their child taken away, or if concerned bystanders, like Bernice in Unit 23, are put off from consulting informally about their concerns. The policy will have to be broad enough to appear welcoming to people who have genuine concerns or who are asking for help, while stringent enough to make sure that determined abusers are not allowed to 'get away with it'.

Help and support may be enough

Allan thought that in some cases where there might be a risk of abuse Donald could be right: that following their usual way of working is all that is needed. A social care assessment under the NHS and Community Care Act 1990 might provide a suitable framework for finding out what is happening and offering more help. However, in other cases, such as the one Allan encountered, what is needed is not a user-friendly assessment but an investigation, involving close work with the police and other agencies.

So far, it seemed to Allan that the policy needed to be a bit like an elastic band stretched round a very large bunch of papers. It had to be 'elastic' enough to hold together:

Workers' need for help	and	Managers' need for control
Room for manoeuvre	and	Formal structures for decision making
Cases where help is an appropriate response	and	Cases where criminal proceedings may be an appropriate response
Cases which can be dealt with in-house	and	Cases which need the input of other agencies
'Domestic' cases	and	Cases in residential care or other public settings

The elastic policy

Key points

- Policies tell workers what to do and procedures set out how they should achieve it.

- Policies must set out what latitude workers have to make their own decisions and when they should follow procedures set down by the service agency.

- There can be conflicts between the needs of workers and the needs of managers in situations of risk or controversy.

Section 2
Learning from personal experience

Allan was beginning to get an idea of the distinction between writing a policy and drawing up procedures, but he was feeling acutely aware of how little he knew about the scale of the problem. How could he begin to get a sense of how much abuse and of what kind might be affecting his department's clients, or affecting others in the local authority's catchment area? Where could he go for reliable information? So far, Allan had been reflecting on his own personal experience and that of his colleagues. How helpful is this kind of knowledge and what are its limitations? Clearly, the group sitting around the table at the meeting had encountered abuse in a number of settings and to a large extent the positions they had taken up in relation to the proposed policy relied on that experience. No one would suggest that what they were saying was not true ... but it may be that it was not the whole truth or the only truth. What problems do you think would be inherent in designing the policy around their views?

Activity 1	**Speaking from experience**
Allow about 5 minutes	Look back over the account of Allan's briefing meeting. How many people are quoted as speaking in the meeting and how many specific cases of abuse are mentioned?

Comment	I listed:

- Donald, who has strong opinions but doesn't mention any specific cases

- Abby, who cites two cases, one of domestic violence involving an older person and the other of a private home care worker who is stealing money

- Allan himself, who has dealt with one case involving a paedophile who sexually abused several boys

- Corinne, who has a view that people who abuse should not be treated as criminals but does not mention any specific cases.

Activity 2	**Limitations of experience**
Allow about 5 minutes	Now jot down five ways in which information based on the experiences of these four people could be incomplete.

Comment	I listed the following:

1   There may have been other cases, which they did not know about.

2   Because some of them are putting across quite strong opinions they might not mention cases which do not accord with or support their views.

3   They do not know what these cases were like for the service users who were abused.

4   They may have forgotten cases which happened a while ago.

5   When they are critical of other staff (for example Allan was cross that
     his colleagues did not record their concerns, and Abby says that
     some of her staff had ignored or explained away warning signals)
     they may not appreciate the pressures on them to act in particular
     ways.

2.1 Partial viewpoints

There are three kinds of problem in using personal experience as the
only basis for making professional judgments. First, it is difficult to tell
how typical your own experience is. For example, Allan has no idea
how often cases like the one he encountered occur. It sticks in his mind
because it was the first case he had to deal with and also because it was
very serious. But it may have been a one-off, and although his policy
will have to be robust enough to deal with such a case, he would not
want to build the whole structure around a case which might not
happen again. So personal experience and anecdotal evidence like this
needs to be put in context.

Second, the accounts may be incomplete and untested. Stories such as
these often unfold over a considerable period of time, and often workers
move on before they hear the outcome of a case. Rumours may prove
unfounded or further facts may come to light. Often information will
only come together at a later stage, at a case conference or court case,
and individuals who have been caught up in the matter earlier may
never *be in a position* to piece together the whole sequence of events.

This phrase 'being in a position to ...' is very significant when evaluating
accounts of events. It encapsulates a key concept: that *knowledge is always
partial and depends on your own position*. It is tempting to think of some
people's knowledge as more accurate or valid than that of others, when
all that is different is the *vantage point* from which they view the issues
under consideration. If you say someone has an 'overview' this is often
taken to mean that their account is well informed and well thought
through: that it is objective and authoritative.

By contrast, when someone is completely immersed in an issue they
may not be able to stand back and view their own experience as if they
were outside looking in. Workers like Marie in Unit 22, and many of the
service users throughout the course, are in this position. You saw in the
Lawler reading in Unit 22 how women workers are often invited to
discount their knowledge because it is so integral to their lived
experience. Yet, someone working with a difficult service user, or one
who is quite ill, might develop a 'sixth sense', picking up subtle changes
of mood or body language. This is a very different kind of knowledge
from that of someone collating details of a hundred cases in order to
find common features. It is as if less powerful people in society and in
the hierarchies of service agencies have an 'underview', and have to
operate from a position where they attend to the particular, as opposed
to operating on the basis of a wider picture. This does not mean that
their view is any the less informed or valid, just different. Later, when
we look at surveys on abuse, you will see that although these sum up a
large number of cases, they do not convey the sense of what it is like to
be abused, or to have to report abuse at first hand. Putting people's
stories together with numbers provides a much more complete account.

Lastly, we can see in the meeting outlined in Section 1.1 that when
people are arguing on the basis of their own experience the facts become
closely woven into layers of interpretation and judgment. Experienced
workers do not just 'clock' cases in their minds; they are all the time

thinking ahead and attaching implications to what they know. They work through examples and draw conclusions. As we saw above, a lot of highly processed information can be gleaned in a short time from this kind of group. But there are risks. Inevitably people are basing their interpretations and conclusions on particular assumptions and stereotypes. For example, in the meeting Corinne is very resistant to the idea that abuse should be criminalised because her picture is of a stressed carer doing his or her best, but we will see later that this is not the whole picture. She does need to add to her information and go back over some of the thinking she has done.

Study skills: Marking the text as you read

In the section you have just read, there was a 'First', 'Second' and 'Last'. Did you think of writing (i), (ii) and (iii) in the margin to show where the three points started? Adding marks in the margin to emphasise the way the argument is structured is often helpful. For example, where an issue is being debated you might write 'For' and 'Against' at suitable points in the margin. Marking the text in this way helps to focus your attention on the argument, as well as making it easier to pick up the thread when you come back later.

2.2 Hearing users

As we have said, one risk of incomplete information is that it misses certain viewpoints. Some people's stories are more easily heard and believed than others. Allan realises that he needs to extend his understanding by seeking the views of other stakeholders, particularly users and survivors of abuse, on whose behalf the policy he is developing will operate. He finds a series of accounts recorded by survivors of abuse in childhood. Although Allan is a fictional character, Ken, whose story you are going to look at now, is real. He is a young man who identifies himself as a survivor both of sexual abuse and of the mental health system. He has also used services for people with learning difficulties, although none of these 'labels' fit him very well. His account of abuse was recorded at a workshop held in 1995 for people with learning difficulties who were survivors of sexual abuse. The workshop was convened to record their stories on tape so that other service users and staff could learn from their experiences. (Edited versions of these interviews can be found in Brown and Stein, 1996, and Stein and Brown, 1996.)

This was a small group, of 10 women and men, and was not representative of all people with learning difficulties who have been abused as children or as adults. The abuse they had suffered was extreme. In most cases it had been at the hands of family members and had lasted throughout their childhoods. They came together as a self-selected group of people who wanted to talk about their lives and use what had happened to them to help others. Before the workshop there was considerable consultation with them and with the staff working with them, to make sure the experience would not be too difficult or traumatic for any of them. Many of those who did decide to come had already been involved in group work with other survivors as a way of working on these issues.

> **Study skills: Understanding what conclusions can be drawn**
>
> These methodological points are important because they help us to *place* these accounts, so that we know the limits of what we can take from them. The case we are going to look at powerfully communicates the emotional pressure which kept someone from disclosing abuse in the context of the public attitudes and service ethos of the time. But you cannot generalise from this one account. To generalise you need a different kind of research based on a large sample, carefully selected to be typical of survivors of childhood abuse.

Ken was in his 30s and had been abused as a child and teenager, so the events he was recounting happened in the late 1960s and early 1970s:

> *Basically what happened to me was my mum and dad split up. Originally I was living with my dad, but in them days the Child Welfare System wasn't very sympathetic to males ... so I was ordered to go and live with my mum. Anyway I went and lived with my mum and my step dad started it, and like he first of all come in and said do you want to have extra pocket money? Of course you wanted to earn extra pocket money didn't you? But I didn't know what was involved at the time and so he started giving me, giving me one up the backside. Getting me to suck him off ... and then he used to whip me and anyway I got – it went on from the age – I was 9 until I was 13. And one night I had had enough, so basically I just went – like, climbed out of the bedroom window, siphoned some petrol out ... I poured all the petrol on his car, bang – set it alight. Anyway in between that I tried to tell my mum and she said you're making it up, because you were sent here by the Court and you don't like [him] anyway. Would you keep his name out of it? Um and you know, no kid makes it up. Anyway we went to Court ... Anyway I got – my sentence was I was sent to a Psychiatric Adolescent Unit – it's now closed – a big hospital just outside [a large town] ... and I was told I was suffering from schizophrenia and delusions. Well they shoved Largactil*

Harry's Drawing

A drawing by a service user attending a workshop for learning disabled survivors of sexual abuse

down me and tried shoving Largactil down me for years and my delusions haven't gone away, and – it just like really angers me that he is still walking the streets ... and then the problem was I ... was fostered, and then when I came out of care I then just wanted to do, like I just kept harming myself because I didn't like myself. It wasn't until about four years ago I was actually believed. [I told] everybody, social workers, doctors, judges ... nobody took any notice. It was a Consultant Psychiatrist actually [who believed me in the end]. She got me psychotherapy ... that's all really ... and got rid of the inappropriate labels that I've got. I've got labels like having a personality disorder ... attention seeking ... and manipulative behaviour. Basically how I've come to tell you about this is, I've learnt to believe in myself, I've used my experience – I've vented my anger in a positive way in the work I'm doing.

(Brown and Stein, 1996)

Allan found this account and the others very moving, and he learnt a lot from them. He was shocked at how difficult it had been for Ken to find someone who would believe him, and at how the social services' response had been to make matters worse by blaming and labelling Ken. But although his first reaction was personal and emotional, it was still possible for him to analyse the account more objectively. Detailed accounts like Ken's can be analysed in terms of processes or stages, which can then be compared with similar cases. For example, not everyone would have to commit arson in order to get their problem taken notice of, but we can speculate that any child being abused at home would try to tell someone, and that if their attempts to tell were not at first successful they might escalate their behaviour.

Secrecy and disclosure are common themes in such accounts. Abuse can end only when a person who is being abused is able to recognise that:

- they are being abused
- it is not their fault or responsibility

and they are able to find someone who will believe them and act for them.

Activity 3   Analysing Ken's story

Allow about 10 minutes   Look back over Ken's story and see if you can sketch out stages he went through.

Comment   I listed the following:

1   Ideology of the official system overrode his wishes ('in them days the Child Welfare System wasn't very sympathetic to males').

2   He became a victim partly because (as a child) he did not have reference points against which to judge that what he was asked to do was wrong ('I didn't know what was involved').

3   His abuser actively attended to keeping the abuse secret ('he used to whip me').

4   He tried to tell a sympathetic adult ('I tried to tell my mum').

5   The response was to disbelieve him ('... and she said you're making it up').

6   He escalated his behaviour until it did result in action ('I poured all the petrol on his car, bang – set it alight').

7   His account was not officially accepted by the court so he was blamed ('my sentence was I was sent to a Psychiatric Adolescent Unit').

8   His credibility was questioned ('I've got labels like having a personality disorder ... attention seeking ... and manipulative behaviour').

9   He found someone who believed him ('it was a Consultant Psychiatrist actually [who believed me in the end]').

10   Once he was believed he was able to 'unsilence' himself and use his experience ('I've learnt to believe in myself, I've used my experience').

Common themes

Although you have to be very careful about making assumptions, other people attending the same workshop did recount similar stories. For example, many had found it difficult to disclose what was happening to them – illness, self-injury, violent behaviour and arson were all described as ways in which they had tried to draw attention to the abuse. One young woman, abused in a foster placement from which she felt she could not escape, swallowed a needle in the aftermath of a serious sexual assault. Several were punished because they tried to tell someone about the abuse, and several had since worked with other survivors of abuse as a way of coming to terms with their experiences.

If we articulate these steps in general terms and set them out in a schematic way, they can be 'looked for' in other accounts (in the way a scientist might repeat an experiment to see if a chemical goes through a pre-ordained series of changes). I translated Ken's experience into the following themes:

- socially created or physical inequalities
- individual isolation and vulnerability
- enforced secrecy and collusion
- attempted disclosure
- individual denial and disbelief
- escalation of attempts at disclosure
- official denial and disbelief
- individual's credibility compromised and used as rationale for disbelief
- powerful ally and witness breaks cycle of disbelief
- 'unsilencing' – experience of abuse accepted and becomes part of individual's identity.

Study skills: Working from individual cases

This method of enquiry, where you start from one example and work outwards, is sometimes referred to as 'grounded theory' (Glaser and Strauss, 1967). As Reichardt and Cook note: 'while a large and diverse sample of cases can aid in forming generalizations so can an in-depth understanding of a single case ...' (1979, p. 15). This kind of 'map' allows us to use individual accounts to structure our thinking, without making assumptions. It provides a series of cues to help us think about what is common and what is particular in each case. It is the kind of opening out of an issue which both practitioners and researchers do in the course of their work.

User accounts tell people like Allan something which they cannot gain from their own professional viewpoint or from larger scale surveys. These are the accounts which are most often silenced, since both past and current abuse is a taboo subject. Allan will certainly have to compare a number of studies to make sure he has reliable information, and he will need to balance the 'what was it like and what do you need?' (qualitative) type of research with the 'how many cases?' (quantitative) type of research. Both types will be useful to him, but each will help him to answer different questions.

Key points

- All knowledge is 'positioned' depending on the vantage point of the person recounting it.

- Individual accounts are partial and incomplete.

- In-depth case studies can suggest themes or processes which help us to analyse other accounts.

- We cannot answer quantitative ('how many?') questions from individual accounts, or small samples, but we can answer qualitative ('what was it like?') questions.

2.3 What is the role of social services?

As Allan began to think about this account, he wondered how his colleagues would and should respond to such situations, and he found himself oscillating between a human and a 'bureaucratic' response. The failure to respond to Ken had been a failure of the *child* protection system, and Allan firmly believed that under the 1989 Children Act the climate had definitely changed and that Ken's allegations would now be properly investigated. But, as Ken is now an adult eligible for community care services on account of his learning difficulties and mental health problems, the social services clearly have a responsibility to take his past experience into account in planning services for him. Yet this was not the prime aim of the adult protection policy, which was designed to pick up and respond to *current* abuse of vulnerable adults, not the legacy of past childhood abuse.

Allen could feel himself slipping into a 'gatekeeper' role and thinking about the stringent eligibility criteria his local authority had just introduced in the face of budget cuts. But he also wondered whether survivors would necessarily *want* any formal intervention from the social services. He would not have wanted anyone to dig into his own family's past. A straw poll of his friends and acquaintances suggested to him that many people overcome past difficulties in their own way and are quite resilient. While the effects of childhood abuse are felt for a long time, many people seem to find their own ways of coping. He found another collection of survivors' stories, *The Memory Bird* (Malone *et al.*, 1996), which backed up this view. He was particularly moved by one woman's account of how she had resolved her feelings. She described how, with support from her family, she confronted her grandfather, who had been responsible for abusing her when she was nine years old. She went to his house with her supporters and read a statement to him detailing what he had done and laying the responsibility clearly at his door.

The Memory Bird

VIRAGO

Survivors of Sexual Abuse

Edited by Caroline Malone, Linda Farthing and Lorraine Marce

'I felt anger at Grandad and pain for myself, and for all women down the ages whose lives have been shattered. I also felt relief and release. A very strong sense of the spiritual, of the rightness of Justice.'(Bennett in Malone et al., 1996, pp. 127–8)

Many survivors of childhood abuse are beginning to favour services based on a self-help model. They see expression rather than suppression with drugs as the most effective route to recovery. Certainly, supporting individuals is not a short-term endeavour. The ripples of abuse can be felt many years or decades afterwards and people have to choose when they are strong enough to deal with it. In Unit 18 Serena, a carer's support worker, said that it could take 'literally years' to persuade someone to come to a carers' group. How much more of a step might it be to acknowledge that one is a survivor of abuse?

Allan was left feeling that alerting services for adults about the legacy of childhood abuse will be a subsidiary part of the policy he is considering, although not its primary purpose. But he could see that for some people childhood abuse and trauma are important precursors of difficulties in adulthood, and this knowledge might feed into a very different kind of service ethos. It might lead one to think, for example, that someone had dealt very well with very difficult circumstances and that if they were struggling and in need of support from the social services, it was because of the gravity of the situation, rather than a deficit in their personalities or coping strategies. This could be very empowering. It recognises the strength individuals bring to their own recovery and places them as the experts in how to deal with exceptional assaults on their integrity rather than as people who have in some way failed to cope. Individuals may then be helped to shift the turmoil they experience in their internal world back on to the outside and reclaim their own sense of control.

2.4 Validating personal accounts

As we saw, Allan's first reaction to Ken's story was to feel angry that he had not been believed. He thought the story 'felt' true, but found himself wondering how he could have verified it. This would be the position of social workers in his agency when faced with disclosures of abuse. Whatever their 'gut feelings', if they wanted to take decisive action against a perpetrator someone would need to be responsible for finding corroborating evidence. Even *supporting* someone like Ken would be difficult if a worker had no objective proof of what he alleged.

As Allan worked through these issues he began to write notes about some of the more practical points which must be spelt out in the policy and procedures. Disclosure was clearly one issue to be flagged up. Allan noted some useful instructions about child protection from official guidance circulated by the government, which he thought could be adapted for adults.

Allan's notes

What to do if a child or vulnerable adult discloses an abusive relationship to you:

- listen rather than directly question

- never stop someone who is freely recalling significant events, in other words don't stop someone in full flow and say: 'hold on, we'll come back to that later', as they may not tell you again

- at the first opportunity make a note of the discussion, which includes the time, the setting, anyone else there and exactly what was said in the person's own words

- date and sign the record.

(Guidance based on the Memorandum of Good Practice, *Home Office in conjunction with the Department of Health, 1992, para. 1.8)*

Verifying people's accounts is an uncomfortable area, but it forms a key part of the response of social service agencies to disclosure. Children and vulnerable adults are vulnerable partly *because* they are liable not to be believed. This then further disadvantages them when they come to seek support or redress. Increasingly, psychological techniques have been applied to verification in a process called 'credibility assessment'. This is beginning to be accepted in courts and other formal proceedings. A vulnerable witness may muddle times or dates but the truthfulness of their account is unlikely to be determined by such details. What is more significant is:

- the amount of detail in the texture of their account

- whether they are using their own words and voice

- whether they recount details, including those which might not have made sense to them at the time

- whether they describe sensations as well as facts, such as what things smelt like or felt like to the touch (see Yuille, 1988).

Also it is worth asking, especially when questioning children or people with learning difficulties, 'If this is not true, how would the person have the knowledge to make it up?'

Activity 4   Credibility assessment

Allow about 5 minutes   Look back over Ken's account. Do you believe him and, if so, why? List five aspects of his statement which seem to you to ring true, or five elements which suggest that his account is not true, using Yuille's technique as a guide.

Comment   1   I thought Ken did use his own words and voice.

2   He described how he got involved in the abuse, for pocket money, and why he stayed involved, because of the whipping.

3   He repeated details of conversations he had with his mum when he tried to tell her about the abuse and she accused him of making it up, saying that he didn't like his stepdad and was telling her about it only because he was sent there by the court.

4   He still expresses his anger at his stepfather: he says he is angry that 'he is still walking the streets'.

5   He also still expresses some fear: 'Would you keep his name out of it', which is consistent with his account of how he suffered in childhood.

In the field of child sexual abuse false accounts have usually been associated with disputed custody hearings (Wakefield and Underwager, 1988, pp. 295–301) and have involved an element of coaching by one of the adults in the child's life. Ken says: 'no kid makes it up', and indeed it is difficult to see in this context what function a false disclosure could serve since the response of the adults in Ken's life had been so punitive. Doubts have sometimes been raised about accounts which emerge in therapy. You saw in Unit 14 how the notion of 'false memories' has been used to imply that therapists may suggest as well as uncover stories of childhood abuse. There may also be some settings in which allegations may be used as a way of wielding control over others, especially if a complainant has seen others gain some advantage as a result of a similar claim. In closed environments such as special hospitals or prisons, where claims and counter-claims may be part of the currency of everyday life, this may be a particular issue. In all settings each and every case has to be evaluated on its merits.

Sometimes, even after a thorough and prompt investigation, it is impossible to come up with independent evidence to support the word of a child or vulnerable adult (especially in cases of sexual crimes which take place in private), and the agency or agencies involved have to sit uncomfortably on the fence. Official agencies such as the social services or the criminal justice system become involved because they are required to act on the judgment they make. They require a different standard of evidence and proof depending on the seriousness of the sanctions they are empowered to impose. Courts have to err on the side of setting a guilty person free rather than imprisoning someone who has not committed a crime, so they require all evidence to be tested through cross-examination and the level of proof to be 'beyond reasonable doubt'. This is stricter than care proceedings, disciplinaries and tribunals held under the Registered Homes Act 1984, which are decided on the basis of the 'balance of probabilities'.

This issue of verification also comes up in the research studies you are going to look at later in this unit. When you are considering the extent of abuse, you have to decide whether you are going to count *all* cases reported or only ones which have been corroborated to a previously defined level of proof. Certainty becomes another issue of definition and thresholds when we decide which cases to include in a particular survey or monitoring exercise. Whether the most inclusive definition is taken or the most stringent will depend on what the information is to be used for. In the box below you can see the criteria for including cases in a large research project I was involved in, on the sexual abuse of adults with learning difficulties (Brown and Turk, 1992). We assigned each report of abuse to one of six categories and we then based most of our figures on the first two categories only. This was not to doubt that some, if not many, of the other cases may have occurred as reported, but since this could not be verified, we decided that it was more important *at that time* to produce information which could not be contested, because many people in influential positions were still denying the significance of abuse in the lives of vulnerable adults. If the purpose of the surveys had been to anticipate how many reports an agency would receive in the next year, then obviously even those which could not be proved would have been included.

---

(1)   Proven/highly probable

Cases where one or more of the following applied:

- forensic evidence of sexual abuse

- the sexual abuse was reliably witnessed

- a formal investigation into the sexual abuse led to significant action being taken against perpetrator or managing agent of the setting where abuse occurred, e.g:
    - successful court conviction
    - staff disciplined and/or dismissed for alleged offence
    - agency/bank staff asked not to return following allegation/concern
    - staff resignation following allegation
    - client(s) or contract withdrawn from service where sexual abuse alleged to have occurred
    - where perpetrator is another client they were removed from setting/agency and/or offered an intervention regarding difficult sexual behaviour
- reliable confession of perpetrator
- any other case with overwhelming evidence

(2)   Probable sexual abuse

These cases were highly suspected where one or more of the following applied:

- an explicit verbal disclosure of sexual abuse which was considered reliable, but in the absence of any corroborating evidence

- there was a court case with insufficient evidence to convict

- at least two of the following pertained:
    - verbal disclosure but concern over victim's reliability of account or their competence to testify
    - partial or unreliable witness
    - significant change in behaviour or emotions
    - medical evidence of physical abuse or of relevant but inconclusive sign, e.g. urinary infection
    - other circumstantial evidence, e.g. torn clothing, alleged perpetrator with known history of sexual offending, clear evidence of access by perpetrator, e.g. in locked room

– involvement of an independent agency to investigate other than the one originally involved, e.g. police.
- registration of residential unit reviewed/monitored at increased intervals following allegation.

(3) Possible sexual abuse

These cases, which we referred to initially as 'rumbling' cases, did not fit the criterion of the previous categories but there was clear ongoing concern that sexual abuse may have occurred/be occurring. Sometimes these were cases where there was evidence for the fact that abuse has taken place but no indication of, or evidence against, a particular perpetrator.

These cases usually met one or more of the following criteria:
- physical abuse with concern over sexual abuse
- a known sexual abuser with access to alleged victim
- known sexual activity with concern over possible exploitation or consent
- inappropriate/unusual sexualised behaviour
- repeated disclosures by victim but these could not be corroborated
- anonymous 'tip-offs'
- any other case where explicit mention of possible sexual abuse has been made at a case conference or between professionals.

(4) Uncertain sexual abuse

This category was used when there was clear evidence of sexual abuse which would have fitted one of the above three categories but for the existence of at least one piece of contradictory or inconsistent information. For example, there may have been an explicit verbal disclosure which was reliable except for one significant anomaly, e.g. victim not at alleged place on alleged day. Similarly, there may have been an allegation that sexual intercourse took place but no forensic evidence, even though the medical examination took place immediately afterwards.

(5) Doubtful sexual abuse

Cases were included here if there was substantial doubt over (a) whether the incident occurred, (b) whether it had a sexual component and/or (c) whether the victim consented.

An example might be where the allegation was felt to be a fantasy and had no basis in reality or where the motive was not sexual (e.g. another resident in a group home hoarding clothes including a 'victim's' pants and bras) or where it was felt the person knowingly and willingly consented to the activity.

(6) Unknown status

Insufficient evidence/information to classify.

This category was used if the person filling in the form had no direct knowledge of the case or was only given access to partial information and hence was not able to reliably assess the likelihood that the incident constituted sexual abuse.

(Adapted from Brown and Turk, 1992)

Activity 5   Assessing Ken's account

Allow about 5 minutes   Look back over Ken's story and see how sure you are about it. In which category would you place it, using the six sets of criteria laid out in the excerpt from Brown and Turk (1992) in the box?

Comment   I would assess Ken's account to be in the 'Probable sexual abuse' category because he has made an explicit verbal disclosure, and because there was demonstrable change in his 'behaviour and emotions'.

You can see from this section that the design of information gathering needs to be tailored to particular needs and tasks. The earliest research studies in a particular area often have a 'claims making' function, in that they publicly make the case that a particular issue is a significant problem which needs to be addressed. For example, it was initially important that the whole argument on sexual abuse was not weakened by including cases which could be refuted; whereas once the importance of the issue had been established, research could move on to focus on clarifying the nature and extent of a particular kind of abuse or abusing, and to explore service responses which work for the people involved.

Key points

- Psychologists can assess the credibility of statements and give evidence about this in court.

- Agencies which are in a position to impose sanctions have to test out individual accounts to a stringent level of proof.

- Criminal cases have to make absolutely sure that they do not mistakenly accept a report of abuse, whereas civil cases and proceedings have slightly more leeway to decide which is the most likely account of events before them.

- Defining the level of certainty attached to reports of abuse is an important stage in research and monitoring.

2.5 A whistle-blower's story

Members of Allan's department have always prided themselves on listening to users and taking their views into account. They have a well-established expectation that there will be user consultation around important issues. However, they have far fewer ways of consulting staff, especially staff in the independent sector, but also direct care staff in their own establishments. Allan stumbles over the whistle-blower's perspective almost by accident, but clearly this is another side of the story, which he must take into account in drawing up a policy that works.

Before long, everyone in Allan's department knew he had taken on the adult protection role and soon he found people coming up to him in the canteen with their stories or opinions. Several days after his initial briefing meeting he sat at the same table as colleagues from the inspection unit and was told the story you are going to hear on the audio cassette. This account is also of an incident which took place in the past, but there are more recent parallels which suggest that not much has changed.

Police launch second abuse probe into South Wales children's homes

Inquiry condems conspiracy of silence at hospital

Again, although Allan is fictional, Adrian, whose story you are going to hear, is real and this incident really happened. Adrian Hughes is now head of a social services' inspection and registration unit, but he started his career as a child care worker in a residential school for children, where he learnt about abuse at first hand.

Activity 6   **Blowing the whistle**

Allow about 30 minutes   Listen now to the interview with Adrian Hughes which you will find on side 2 of Audio Cassette 6. In the first part of the interview you will hear Adrian describe how difficult it was for him to report this abuse and get it put on the record, but he then goes on to say how, in his current practice as an inspector, he attempts to overcome some of those pressures.

When you have listened to the whole interview go back to the beginning and jot down all the reasons Adrian gives as to why he found it difficult to be a whistle-blower.

Comment   My list looks like this:

- Adrian was new and, as he said, 'a bit green'.
- He didn't have much status in the home.
- He felt 'part of the abuse' because he had asked the senior worker for help and he had been drawn into it by holding his colleague's watch.
- He was put off by a senior worker who challenged his judgment and inexperience.
- He didn't want to jeopardise his livelihood or his future career.
- He didn't know whom he could go to outside the establishment.

Adrian was not able to confront the abuse partly because he had been drawn into it himself. We considered this as a problem in the health warning in Section 1 of Unit 23. And we saw from Marie's experience too that, especially when workers did not have any formal induction, they were reliant on the way older and more senior workers set up and demonstrated the work to them. We saw that Marie was drawn into a session of joke telling which she found particularly uncomfortable and which, we can speculate, she would have found very difficult to report.

Worried something is going seriously wrong in your workplace? Not sure what to do?

Whether you plan to say nothing or to blow the whistle, talk to us first in <u>strict confidence</u> and <u>without obligation</u>. Public Concern at Work is a charity which offers <u>free</u> legal advice to people concerned about serious malpractice at work.

Phone 0171 404 6609

Support for whistle-blowers

When Adrian did eventually say something to a manager who was senior both to him and to the worker who had abused the child, what he said was discounted. His lack of status in the home and the lack of agreed guidelines worked against his complaint being taken seriously by management. Adrian did question the actions of his senior but was told that the way this incident had been handled might have been 'appropriate'. Adrian described this as a 'conspiracy' of senior staff. Although a clear hierarchy existed, the management did not offer guidance or support – a feature identified by Wardaugh and Wilding in the Course Reader, Chapter 24, which you read at the end of Unit 22.

Adrian felt inhibited from pursuing his complaint because he was afraid he would lose his livelihood and, as he said, he had rent to pay and food to buy. Being a whistle-blower involves taking risks which cut into the very basics of life. It can involve being intimidated, threatened or harassed. To take a complaint outside an establishment, you also have to know your way around the social services and know 'what the next steps would be'. You have to know whom you can go to; who will be impartial and able to act.

Adrian's story brings together a number of themes which have come up in this block.

Adrian said that the establishment was not a 'listening' regime. It was also not a regime with explicit guidelines for staff on how to handle difficult behaviour or complicated situations. As an inspector now going into services Adrian has translated what he knows about good practice into a set of indicators he now routinely looks out for. He mentioned:

- staff meetings
- review meetings to discuss how to respond to particular children or residents
- a clear record of any sanctions taken
- guidance, professional input or training on how to deal with difficult behaviour, such as that of Rosalie, whom you read about in Unit 22, Section 2.

You may be able to think of other indicators.

Adrian learnt the hard way, from his experience as a whistle-blower whose whistle was not heard. Pilgrim (1995, pp. 81–2) highlights two kinds of whistle-blowing:

> *The first is where a professional draws attention to the conduct of colleagues which **violates** norms ... the second is where a professional **challenges** the norm itself and thereby raises the question of whether it should be changed.*

Which type do you think Adrian was faced with? I think he started out thinking that he needed to do the former, but then found he would have to do the latter. He started by thinking that the behaviour he had witnessed would be as unacceptable to his managers as it was to him, but his manager's response made it clear that his colleague's abusive behaviour *conformed* to the prevailing view of how to deal with such incidents. Adrian had come up against the proverbial brick wall: to take his complaint further would have involved challenging the whole regime and its values – a very difficult thing for a new worker to do. Another argument for having clear and explicit guidelines in services is that they allow breaches to be more easily reported. If workers are clear that an action *should* not have happened, then they only have to report that it *did* happen. They do not have to challenge or try to redefine the way things are done. Allan made some notes about what whistle-blowers need.

Allan's notes

It is no use having a policy if direct care staff like Adrian don't get to hear about it. We will have to publicise it to all staff across the whole range of services.

Whistle-blowers need to know whom to go to if their own manager won't deal with their complaints. We must build a back-up into the systems.

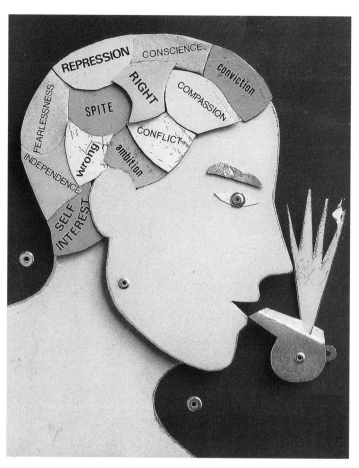

Blowing the whistle isn't easy

Key points

- It can be very difficult for direct care workers to challenge the bad practice of colleagues or senior workers.

- Whistle-blowers may report on rules that have been broken but they may also have to challenge the rules themselves.

- Regulators need to actively look for indicators of openness and consultation especially in relation to the use of sanctions.

- To make effective complaints or to report abuse, workers need to know what steps they should take both inside and outside their immediate agency.

2.6 Consulting records

Allan's next task is to consult the department's own records and information systems and come up with estimates of the extent of adult abuse. In children's services the department puts out an annual statement of the number of children put on the 'at-risk' register, so the number of cases being monitored can be seen at a glance. In adult services the idea of a register has not been adopted. Allan thinks it would be too intrusive. But he expected that records of some kind would be available in adult services, even if these were more informal. He thought that if he could find out how many cases they dealt with last year, he could use that as the basis for his projections. He started with the two mental health teams, because their office was in the same building and he had already had several conversations with Donald after his initial briefing meeting. He started out thinking this bit would be easy but he soon found that he had stirred up another hornet's nest.

Although the two teams serve roughly the same size populations, they had very different views of the amount of abuse affecting their clients. Neither had a formal system for recording the information, but one team leader said they hardly ever got any cases, whereas the other said her team were dealing with abuse 'on a daily basis'. Which was true, and how could their views be so far apart?

Activity 7 **How much abuse?**

Allow about 10 minutes Make a list of the factors which might affect each team in their assessment of the extent of abuse affecting their clients.

Comment I thought of these:

- The teams may serve different kinds of area: for example, one team might cover an inner-city neighbourhood and the other a more rural or affluent area, so that the former serves a greater proportion of homeless people, which is reflected in higher rates of abuse.

- They might have a different idea of what Allan means by 'abuse'; in other words, they might be using different definitions and thresholds.

- They might have a different outlook on why people use mental health services; one team might have a more 'medical' approach, whereas the other might think of mental ill health as linked to abuse, or other traumatic life experiences, and specifically ask about them.

- One team might provide services which specifically attract people who have been, or are currently being, abused.

- One team might be more sensitive (perhaps even too alert) to their clients' past traumas and listen more to what they have to say.

Did you think of any other factors? Certainly this means that we cannot take estimates about the level of abuse at face value. In reading different studies we have to consider very carefully the context within which data have been collected.

Allan met with Donald, the principal officer for mental health, to discuss the difficulty of recognising and then keeping good records about abuse. Donald touched on several issues we discussed in Units 22 and 23, about difficulties in definition and thresholds. He said that although there was a lot of evidence that previous abuse was a factor in mental ill health, practitioners often did not know whether they should ask about it (Williams *et al.*, 1993). He also echoed some of the particular concerns around consent which you looked at in Unit 22 – how capacity to consent might vary over time, so that someone might be quite independent usually but at other times become more vulnerable. This made it difficult to decide who should be seen as a 'vulnerable' adult at any one time, which was not so much of a problem in relation to other client groups. One possibility Donald discussed was that they should formally apply the policy only in cases involving someone who had been sectioned (that is, detained under the 1983 Mental Health Act). If a more inclusive approach was taken, he said, it would be difficult to make consistent judgments across different settings. The teams' clients had a wide range of living situations, including living in their own homes (alone or with family members/carers), in residential care, in acute psychiatric wards or on the streets. He said there were particularly high rates of abuse for people living rough, especially if they were misusing alcohol or drugs.

Allan felt a bit frustrated by this. He was concerned that a history of abuse may become hidden in the process of mental health diagnosis. One of the first papers Dave produced for him confirmed this (Rose *et al.*, 1991). It examined the personal histories of 89 clients referred to a new intensive case management service, in New York, for long-term users of mental health services. You would expect people in this situation to have thick files built up over years of involvement with service agencies, so it is perhaps surprising that in this mass of information there was a resounding silence when it came to consideration of abuse and trauma in their lives, whether that abuse was in childhood and therefore a possible background to their mental health problems, or happening to them now in their adult lives and thus important information for current service providers.

However, when the researchers *specifically asked* about and looked for abuse as a factor in people's lives they found it was very prevalent. Of the people qualifying for this service (on account of the complexity and long-standing nature of their mental health problems), half were adult children of alcoholic parents and, *when asked*, about one-third disclosed that they were survivors of childhood sexual abuse. People who self-injure, and those whose reliance on mental health services was the most intense, were the most likely to have a prior history of serious abuses which were 'violent, prolonged or intrusive' and/or perpetrated by a primary caretaker. The authors of the study saw this failure to ask about abuse as a critical blind spot. They argue that: 'by not initiating a discussion of abuse, professionals may unwittingly confirm their patients' belief in the need to deny the reality of their experience' (p. 41).

STOP NO EVIL

If services fail to appreciate the importance of abuse as a factor in why people seek help, these people's stories will not figure in their understandings of abuse, or in more systematic monitoring. This makes it difficult to interpret findings about the extent of abuse. A high rate of reporting might result from active efforts to provide opportunities for disclosure, whereas a service with few abuse reports may *either* be working successfully to protect people, *or* be oblivious to distress and the misuse of authority. Higher reporting rates may be indicative of a more supportive rather than a more abusive service.

Allan revised his opinion of the two mental health teams. He decided that the team who recognise that they are dealing with abuse on a daily basis may be the most sensitive to the needs and lives of their service users, whereas the other team may not be seeing what they do not want to see. What did you think? Allan added to his notes about what needs to be in the policy.

Allan's notes

We need a cue in the standard social care assessment to make sure workers ask about any abuse in someone's past or if they need help now, and ...

... we need to monitor individual cases and collate figures from each team.

Key points

- Problems of definition and lack of clarity about thresholds may interfere with routine monitoring.

- Service users are often not asked about their experiences of abuse and trauma even though they are asked other personal questions in the process of diagnosis and assessment.

- Not asking means that abuse is not dealt with as an issue for individuals and for the service.

- High reporting of abuse may be an indicator of sensitivity to service users and not a consistent measure of actual abuse.

Section 3
Shaping up the policy

Ken and Adrian's stories, together with the discussion Allan has had with the mental health teams, have given him some clear messages about what policies and procedures need to achieve. Without policies:

- Ken and other survivors were not believed, or protected from further abuse, or helped to recover

- Adrian and other less powerful staff were not able to question coercive regimes, or put their concerns on the record

- the service as a whole was not gathering information that could be used to inform practice.

Policies first of all need to state clearly where the boundaries lie in relation to physical control, sexual contact, financial transactions and personal interaction, by developing the kind of guidance Vicky Golding spoke about in Unit 22. But then they need to spell out, as Adrian says, 'what you do about it' and set up channels which guarantee formal as well as informal 'links to the outside world'.

3.1 Different roles

Taking Adrian's story as an example, six key organisational responses are needed if children or vulnerable adults are to be protected:

- alerting
- reporting
- allocating
- investigating
- making decisions
- monitoring.

This kind of framework was set out in a document on the sexual abuse of adults that was produced by two voluntary organisations for the Social Services Inspectorate: ARC (The Association of Residential Communities) and NAPSAC (The National Association for the Prevention of Sexual Abuse of Adults and Children with Learning Disabilities) (1993). It was meant to act as a model for other agencies who were just beginning to think the issues through. The report was called *It Could Never Happen Here*: reflecting the 'head in the sand' attitude of many agencies to the risk of abuse in their services.

Alerting

First, individual staff need to be alert to abuse and clear about what constitutes abuse. Then they need to know how, and to whom, they should make a report. Most staff are not in a position to prove what has happened, nor powerful enough to launch a major challenge to current practice or values. So they need to feel able to report even vague concerns, rather than present a watertight case. Adrian mentioned that while he was at the children's home there were rumours about sexual abuse which later led to a conviction. Junior staff like Adrian were not in a position to investigate or verify these suspicions, nor would it have been appropriate for them to start acting as amateur sleuths. It should have been enough for them to have reported their concern, confident that this would be investigated impartially by someone who would not have divided loyalties or be embedded in the dynamics of this particular workplace.

Turning a concern into an official report

The job of first line managers is to turn the concern into a written and official report, thereby triggering a response from the system of interlocking agencies who work with children or vulnerable adults. We also saw from Adrian's experience that this process needs to include some safeguards, not only for the 'alerter' in terms of their own position and safety, but also in terms of back up in case the person to whom the alerter voices their concerns fails to act on it. A policy, by its tone and content, should seek to tip the balance in favour of reporting by safeguarding the rights of individual workers like Adrian, who want to pass on concerns without risking their jobs or references.

In the USA several states have statutes which:

- take the discretion out of reporting by making it against the law *not to report* concerns about a vulnerable adult

- provide limited compensation to anyone who loses their job as a result of reporting concerns to the appropriate authority

- pool information across the several agencies involved so that a co-ordinated investigation can take place

- put individual care and protection packages in place to support anyone who has been the victim of abuse.

Most adult protection policies in the UK attempt to do the same, although they do not carry the same legal weight as these American statutes or as child protection procedures.

Key differences between adults and children are that, for children, reporting concerns and pooling information between agencies are mandatory, whereas for adults, information is transferred between agencies on what is called a 'need to know' basis. This must be thought through in each individual case. Moreover, adults who are vulnerable but still independent and who do not lack capacity to make their own decisions may choose to opt out of any procedures which seem too heavy-handed or distressing to them, and this would need to be respected. The caring services have a much firmer mandate to act for children where their safety is at issue.

Allocating

A decision has to be made about what kind of investigation should take place. This will determine not only the level of the person to whom it is assigned within social services, but also which agency will take the lead. In the type of case Corinne has in mind it seems appropriate for a care manager to augment the social care assessment and provide a little extra help. But in a case involving, say, serial sexual abuse in a residential home for people with learning difficulties or mental health problems, the police and the inspection unit would have a more central role. Allan's policy must set out to whom the initial written report will go, so that this decision can be made by someone experienced and appropriately senior.

Investigating

A process of assessment and/or investigation must then take place in which information is pooled and evidence sought. Whoever takes the lead must ensure that all relevant information is shared, and that the investigation is carried out by people who have the necessary special skills and knowledge. In complicated cases the investigation will need to be very carefully managed and co-ordinated because so many issues and agencies are involved. The main goal is to establish matters of fact. After that, different agencies have different jobs to do. Each agency has a distinct responsibility to act in relation to:

- the person who has been victimised (usually the social services)
- the perpetrator (sometimes the police or personnel)
- the establishment (often the inspection unit, contracts managers or purchasers).

The co-ordinator should make sure that interviews are not repeated by different agencies and that all relevant resources and legal powers are used in the interest of the person who has been abused, or are brought to bear on the person who is thought to have perpetrated the abuse. The main aim is to ensure the safety of the victim, and other previous or potential victims of the perpetrator.

Making decisions

The findings of this investigation will probably be summed up at a case conference, at which it will be decided how best to protect the individual, support them, help them to recover and protect others who might be at risk. This might involve putting in place more support for the person who is responsible for the abuse; the perpetrator might, for example, be a carer who cannot cope (Corinne's scenario). Alternatively, in cases such as the one Allan was concerned about, where it was important for the perpetrator not to 'get away with it', it might involve sanctions such as prosecution, disciplinary proceedings or action under the Registered Homes Act 1984. These two approaches are characterised by Bennett and Kingston (1993) as 'compassion' as opposed to 'control' strategies. If the allegations have proved to be unfounded, then the person against whom abuse was alleged may need careful support to help them get back to normal, especially if this involves returning to a work place from which they have been suspended under a cloud.

This stage may not be handled very well. Families who have been the subject of child protection work are often left in limbo. While removal of the child's name from the register is one outcome, which 'returns parents, somewhat tyrannised, to the ranks of the orthodox' (Dartington Social Research Unit, 1995, p. 38), it may leave matters of fact and future plans unstated:

> *In common with many other social systems, while professionals jealously guard the point of entry, less attention is given to the point of exit ... leaving this system is rarely tidy ... some lingering ambiguity is to be expected.*

> *(Dartington Social Research Unit, 1995, p. 38)*

In adult protection, where responsibilities are even less clear, strategies for closing the case, or for leaving it open to be monitored, are much less developed. A critical issue is often deciding to whom information could and should be passed if there is a concern about continuing risk. This usually hinges on striking a balance between confidentiality and public interest (as discussed in Unit 19) and then ensuring that information is only passed between agencies on a 'need to know' basis. This dilemma does not arise in relation to child protection work, where the interests of the child are always held to be paramount in decisions of this kind.

Monitoring

A further task, as Allan has already identified, will be monitoring, both at an individual and an agency level, so that vigilance can be maintained over time on behalf of individuals at risk, and also so that accurate planning can be done on the basis of records which are more systematic than those held by Donald's mental health teams (ARC/ NAPSAC, 1993, pp. 45–60).

Allan's notes

The adult protection policy will identify who is responsible for the following tasks:

- **alerting:** that is, passing on a concern to a senior person, either inside or, if necessary, outside the 'alerter's' own establishment or agency

- **reporting:** that is, making an official record of the alert and triggering action under the procedures

- **allocating the case:** that is, someone senior needs to decide what level of response is appropriate and which agency is best placed to lead the investigation

- **investigating:** that is, co-ordinating the gathering of information and the conduct of interviews, consulting other appropriate agencies to establish matters of fact and deciding how best to protect the vulnerable adult

- **decision making:** a case conference needs to be called to decide what to do next and who needs to know, to keep this person safe and protect others who might be at risk

- **monitoring:** means keeping track of individual cases, making decisions through case conferences and gathering information about adult protection work as a whole.

3.2 Different functions

Deciding who should do what within social services agencies is not only a matter of levels within the hierarchy, but of specialist expertise and the specific functions of assessors, purchasers, regulators and providers. There is also a job to be done in deciding how to allocate responsibilities *across* the different agencies. For example, the police often take a central role in child and adult protection investigations and train alongside social workers in joint interviewing techniques. Police authorities are also the only ones who are authorised to keep information on file about suspected abusers. Inspection units are increasingly involved in following up concerns about bad practice or abuse in residential homes. You may find that arrangements in your area differ from those in neighbouring authorities and relate to equivalent but different structures within health trusts and other NHS structures.

Activity 8   Who does what?

Allow about 15 minutes   Imagine you are the keyworker for an adult with learning difficulties in a residential home, who has recently made a formal complaint about being hit by a member of staff. This has been backed up by two independent witnesses, so the facts are not in doubt. Can you explain to your client exactly what each of the following people or agencies would be responsible for as his or her complaint is processed? Jot down what you would say about:

(a)   your client's care manager

(b)   the manager of the residential home

(c)   the social services contracts manager

(d)   the inspection unit

(e)   the police.

Comment   Let's take these in turn, as each has a different focus:

(a)   Your care manager is responsible for deciding with you what is best and paying for the care you need. They might want to talk to you about whether you would like to move, given what has happened, and whether you want some counselling or specific support to help you get over this. They may accompany you to any interviews and speak up for you in any meetings held to make decisions.

(b)   The manager of the residential home will have to co-operate with the investigation being carried out by the inspection unit. They will probably dismiss the person who hit you, and they may have to make sure it doesn't happen again by being more careful about interviewing people who come to work at the home, or by making sure they don't use people from the agency all the time.

(c)   The social services contracts manager will write down all the things the manager of the residential home has to do. If the home's manager doesn't do all these things, the contracts manager will stop paying for people to come to the home and it will close down.

(d)   The inspection unit is in charge of finding out what exactly happened and why you were treated this way. The inspectors will tell the manager of the residential home what to do to change the place so that this never happens again. If the manager does not do what they are told to do, then the inspectors may take legal action to force them to make the changes, or close the home down.

(e)   The police may bring a case against the person who hit you, and then there will be a court case. Everyone will say what happened to you, and a jury will decide whether the person who hit you should be fined or sent to prison for hurting you in this way.

Interagency working is complicated, but the goal of an adult protection policy must not be lost in the detail. The aim is to stop the abuse from happening again to this person (or to another vulnerable adult or child) and to help the person recover. Later in the unit we will be looking at the service needs of people who have been abused, but here we have dwelt more on the processes of accountability which allow various authorities to intervene when concerns are expressed.

Key points

- Different members of staff should have responsibility for alerting, reporting, allocation of cases, investigating, decision making and monitoring cases involving abuse.

- When carrying out an investigation into abuse, you need to keep a separate focus on supporting the victim, acting against the perpetrator and identifying service improvements and safeguards.

- Concerns should be monitored over time, especially in inconclusive cases.

- Information about cases involving abuse should be collated at agency level to provide accurate information for planning.

Section 4
Learning from research

You have seen how Allan's consultations have helped him develop the shape of his policy and procedures, but there are still large gaps in his knowledge. Although he has gleaned a lot of information and opinion about the issues from different stakeholders in the service network, none of the information has been collected systematically. Allan has had to guess how it fits in with the wider picture; he has had to use his common sense to judge whether the cases he has heard about are typical. He still does not have information about the extent of abuse or about patterns of victimisation or abusing. By this stage, the papers Dave ordered from the library have arrived and Allan has decided to shut his office door and do some concentrated reading.

Study skills: Reading research critically

As Allan does his research into patterns of abuse and service needs, you can follow his progress and learn with him how to interpret research reports critically. As you read the research, you need to ask yourself questions about how the authors have collated the information they are reporting, how accurate it might be, why one author's figures don't look quite the same as another's and so on.

We call these issues 'methodological' in that they are about the *methods* used in research – how investigations are carried out, how data are analysed and presented and how findings are written up. You can usually see methodological details quite near the beginning of a paper, where the author sets out exactly how a study was carried out. For example, a study of abuse should include:

- definitions of abuse
- details of the population under consideration; for example, if the study concerns older people, what age range it covers; if it concerns people with learning difficulties, what types of people are being included in this category
- definition of the wider population or catchment area; for example, if abuse reports within a certain geographical area are being logged, what is the general population and demographic make-up of that area
- from whom the information was gathered
- how the information was gathered – that is, who asked whom and in what format.

The principles of how the study was carried out should be transparent, so you could in theory repeat the exercise, to see whether your home town has the same level of reported abuse, or whether your service is picking up as many cases as the service which was researched.

We have seen that awareness of abuse is dependent on the attitudes of workers, and this inevitably feeds into research reports, biasing the results. Different amounts of abuse will be reported, and possibly different types, depending on the level of enquiry and the methodology used. One way of looking at the different kinds of information accessed can be seen in the pyramid diagram in Figure 1, which illustrates how information about abuse might be filtered out. Studies which 'plug in' to different levels of the system are bound to arrive at different estimates. Even when the same definitions of abuse are used and consistently applied, a very different picture will emerge if you interview service users, or people at various points in the hierarchy of service providers, purchasers, inspectors and representatives of the criminal justice system.

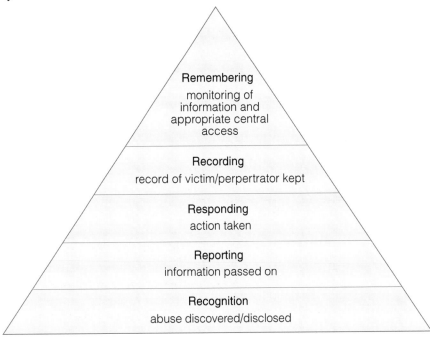

Figure 1
Different levels of acknowledgement of abuse (Turk and Brown, 1994, p. 196)

The most inclusive information is likely to be obtained when *recognition* of abuse is not dependent on the alertness or interpretation of others, but is gathered directly from children or vulnerable adults themselves. But even then, if clients do not disclose incidents, these will remain hidden and will not register in studies or reports. When carers or care workers are asked instead, their sensitivity will be a factor, as we have seen above. They may miss cases by not asking or by failing to pick up signals, or they may actively screen information out by disbelieving people or not considering abuse an issue worthy of their attention. Even if abuse is recognised it may not be consistently *reported* or collated, as we saw in the mental health teams described above, or the information may stay as a note on a personal file rather than be fed into a service-wide picture of abuse and related needs. And for an appropriate *response* to be made, information has to be passed to the right person or agency.

Reading the research papers, then, is not going to be a straightforward exercise. It is not possible to say: 'Well, 10 per cent of people have been abused and that's that'. You will have to read between the lines and behind the figures to see what has influenced the final results. As well as looking at what each study shows, you have to think about what it might have missed.

Quantitative and qualitative research

The research ahead of you has an emphasis on numbers. This is called 'quantitative' research (i.e. finding out quantities). It is contrasted with 'qualitative' research, such as the studies you read earlier, which drew on victims' own accounts of their experiences. When research is mentioned in public, it is often quantitative research that people have in mind. It has a more 'scientific' image (not mere words but 'hard facts'). Yet all branches of science have always relied on a mix of both kinds of research. You cannot tell what to count unless you also spend time observing, describing and trying to understand. In any case, numbers can be misleading. A number is not a 'fact'. As you will see, different studies may produce very different numbers, which purport to represent the same fact. Quantitative research is important, but it is not necessarily more reliable or more 'factual' than qualitative research. Both need to be approached in a cautious, questioning way. Look back quickly at the section 'Not all data are numbers' on pages 105–6 of *The Good Study Guide*.

4.1 Incidence and prevalence

Allan's first bundle of papers is concerned with the sexual abuse of adults with learning difficulties. He has several different articles and he is irritated to find that each gives completely different kinds of figures, and that some give percentages while others give numbers. Sometimes estimates are expressed in terms of the chances any one individual has of being abused, or taken ill, over their lifetime. This is called a 'prevalence' study, and is expressed either as a percentage or a rate per 1,000. Alternatively, the number of new cases within a specific catchment area or population can be estimated, and this is called an 'incidence' study. To make sense of the different studies he makes a clear note for himself that:

> - prevalence studies tell you how many people have experienced abuse, and
>
> - incidence studies tell you how many new cases there are in an area over a given time period.

Occasionally one study will give both figures. He decides to separate the papers into prevalence studies and incidence studies as far as possible. First he looks at the prevalence studies on sexual abuse of adults with learning difficulties. He finds that there is still a wide variation in the figures, so he makes himself a list summarising the results:

1   An American prevalence study asked people with learning difficulties about abuse: 65 out of 95 people attending a day centre were interviewed (Hard and Plumb, 1987), and 38 of the 65 (58 per cent) reported that they had been sexually abused during their lifetime, 83 per cent of the women and 32 per cent of the men.

2   A more recent study by McCarthy and Thompson (1997) drew on a sample of people referred to a sex education/counselling service. The authors based their figures on detailed interviewing as well as review of case notes. They came up with figures of 61 per cent of women and 25 per cent of men who had been previously sexually abused.

3 Buchanan and Wilkins (1991) got their information from front-line staff working with children and adults aged 8–45 and arrived at a figure of 8 per cent prevalence.

4 Cooke (1990) surveyed psychiatrists and estimated prevalence of 4.5 per cent.

To help him compare the figures given in the different studies Allan draws up the table shown here as Table 1.

Table 1 Prevalence studies on sexual abuse

	Abuse reported by:			
	People with learning difficulties		Care staff	Psychiatrists
	(study 1)	(study 2)	(study 3)	(study 4)
Estimated prevalence	83% women 32% men	61% women 25% men	8%	4.5%

There are problems in comparing these studies, since they used different definitions as well as different methodologies, but it would seem that care staff in residential and day services were aware of almost twice as many cases as psychiatrists. However, it is at the first hurdle – getting staff to recognise and believe the experiences of people with learning difficulties – that the largest drop in awareness is seen. This confirms the picture Allan took away from his informal consultations, that there is a pool of abuse not picked up by service agencies. The further away you get from direct contact with service users, the less abuse is known about, as cases are effectively filtered out at each layer of the system (Brown, 1994).

We can guess that Allan would also have found different estimates of the incidence of abuse among mental health service users in his local authority if he had consulted service users, or direct care workers, rather than the team leaders in his building. Had there been a consistent policy on recording incidents, or perhaps a way of accessing all the cases where abuse had been noted from a computerised database, he would have been able to plan next year's services on the basis of this year's activity. His aim is to reach a point where the department produces its own information to help staff to:

• learn about the risks to, and vulnerability of, particular groups and take these into account in planning services

• plan service provision for people who have been abused – services such as safe houses and specialist counselling

• plan service provision for people who abuse, especially if they are other service users in their own right, or carers entitled to a separate assessment of their own needs

• build appropriate preventive measures into the processes of contracting, registration and the management of residential care homes.

But until they have that information from their own records he needs to access it through research studies and reports which have tapped into other agencies and networks.

> **Key points**
>
> • Researching abuse is complex because not all cases are recognised as 'abuse', or recorded as such.
>
> • Increases in reporting may reflect greater awareness rather than more actual abuse.
>
> • Research studies tend to use different sources of information and different approaches, which makes them difficult to compare.
>
> • Prevalence studies record the proportion of people abused over their lifetime, whereas incidence studies note the number of new cases per 1,000 which come to light in a given time period.

4.2 Patterns of abuse – sexual abuse of adults with learning difficulties

Before Allan tidies the papers on learning difficulties away he jots down some of the common factors which have emerged because, despite their different ways of gathering information, there are areas of agreement. He makes notes based mainly on the findings of a study into *reported* cases of sexual abuse involving adults with learning difficulties as recalled by senior managers in statutory services (Brown et al., 1995). You have already read about the definitions of consent and certainty adopted for this study (Brown and Turk, 1992). The study was carried out just before the change to a mixed economy of care had taken root, when health and social services were still the main providers of care. Senior managers were asked to complete a form for anyone using their service whom they knew to have been the *victim* of sexual abuse in the previous two-year period.

The study was comprehensive in that all the major agencies across an entire regional health authority agreed to take part in the survey, although their commitment varied in terms of ensuring that all completed forms were returned. The study produced an estimate of incidence rather than prevalence. It was expressed as the number of new cases per year per 1,000 of the general population. If reporting were to stay at the level calculated you might expect 6–8 cases in a health district serving a population of 225,000, and that something of the order of 1,250 people with learning difficulties in the UK would be sexually abused each year.

People reported as having been abused in this study were mostly abused by people they knew, not strangers. Of the perpetrators, 96 per cent were men and they abused slightly more women than men. In 140 out of the 169 (83 per cent) proven or highly suspected cases the perpetrator was known and familiar to the victim and a part of their social network or routine. In 22 cases the perpetrator was a family member, 21 were other known and trusted adults, 29 were members of staff or volunteers, and other service users were the perpetrators in 80 cases. You can see that other service users were the most frequently named group (almost half the cases). However, they might have been more likely to have been reported than other abusers because they were more often witnessed abusing. Other studies, including the one mentioned above (McCarthy and Thompson, 1997) based on detailed interviews with people receiving sex education, have suggested a higher proportion of family members as abusers; the Brown *et al.* (1995) study did not find many abusers who were family members, but it focused on services which tend not to have much contact with the families of adults who use day and residential services. Staff and volunteers accounted for one-fifth of the cases, but they might also be under-represented. This is partly because they have the power to keep abuse secret, but also because, even if abuse had come to light, the perpetrator's manager might have decided simply to let them resign, in which case they would not have been included in these figures.

The largest group of 'alerters', about two-thirds, were people with learning difficulties themselves. This has also been found in other research studies. In McCarthy and Thompson's work it was significant that service users often told the interviewer about abuse but did not actually name it as such themselves. They recounted abusive or violent incidents, but without appreciating what the authors called the 'social meaning' of what they were disclosing. This raises concerns for people who cannot speak for themselves, and points to a need to train care staff to be sensitive and to listen carefully.

This research has had a significant impact on the way services approach sexuality issues, and has made them more cautious about consent and about recruitment. Some of the findings challenged 'common sense' and certainly got sexual abuse on the agenda. It had been overlooked and simply not talked about in services until about 1989. A key finding was the high proportion of abuse perpetrated by other service users. This prompted the government to fund a further policy document looking at how services should meet the needs of service users who abuse others, as well as those who have been abused (Churchill *et al.*, 1997). Another important development was the more open acknowledgement of the abuse *of* men and the predominance of men as abusers, especially those who were known to the victim, as opposed to strangers. Sexual abuse is often framed as a 'women's issue' but many men are also affected. Previous sex education programmes with material on personal safety had focused on 'stranger-danger', rather than the problems of dealing with unwanted sexual contact from men you know. Without this exercise in bringing together information across a number of services and a wide geographical area, practitioners would only have had access to isolated incidents, and patterns would not have been discernible.

Key points

- Both women and men with learning difficulties are at risk of sexual abuse.

- Perpetrators are mostly men who are known to them and part of their networks.

- Other service users were the largest group of abusers, although abuse was also perpetrated by staff and volunteers, family members and other known and trusted adults.

- Abuse by strangers was rare.

- The abuse came to light mostly because of their own disclosure.

4.3 Patterns of abuse – incidence and patterns of elder abuse

Allan moved on from this issue to consider a much larger study, which aimed to reveal an accurate picture of the actual (as opposed to reported) abuse of older people within a specific catchment area. This study was rigorously designed to try to eliminate some of the biases we have talked about above. The authors, Pillemer and Finkelhor (see Offprint 34), were very aware of the limitations of research when it depends on service reports. They designed this study to 'cut out the middleman', by asking older people (or their carers) directly about abuse so that they did not have to rely on cases which had been reported to a social services agency.

Activity 9 **Elder abuse: a worked example**

Allow about 40 minutes

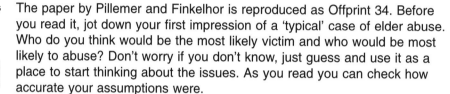

The paper by Pillemer and Finkelhor is reproduced as Offprint 34. Before you read it, jot down your first impression of a 'typical' case of elder abuse. Who do you think would be the most likely victim and who would be most likely to abuse? Don't worry if you don't know, just guess and use it as a place to start thinking about the issues. As you read you can check how accurate your assumptions were.

Now read Offprint 34.

(a)   When you have finished, look back at the section on definitions. Would you include anything else?

(b)   Then find the paragraph which tells you how these results compare with earlier studies of elder abuse which relied on *reports from service agencies*. What three risk factors did this study confirm?

(c)   Name at least two new discoveries revealed by the study.

Comment   (a)   The study includes physical abuse, emotional abuse and neglect but not sexual abuse. Do you think this is because sexual abuse is not a problem for older people? I think it is because this has yet to be acknowledged as an issue, and that if it had been specifically asked about the researchers might have found some cases, possibly associated with other types of abuse. Stevenson (1996) shares this view, saying that:

It is well recognised that feelings about sexuality in old age are, to put it mildly, ambivalent. Thus the likelihood of abuse being denied, ignored or minimised are even greater than in childhood. It seems highly probable that, as awareness of abuse generally increases and domestic violence becomes increasingly unacceptable, referrals for sexual abuse of old people, as of other vulnerable adults, will climb rapidly and will prove one of the areas which is most contentious and complex.

(Stevenson, 1996, p. 28)

(b)   Pillemer and Finkelhor found that older people who are abused are more likely to be:
- living with someone else
- in poor health
- isolated and without close contacts.

This confirmed the view from samples of reported abuse, but Pillemer and Finkelhor suggest that these samples tend to come from more deprived sections of the community because these groups are more visible to welfare agencies.

(c) (i) More abuse is perpetrated by *spouses* than by sons or daughters. Of the abuse identified in this study 58 per cent was perpetrated by spouses as opposed to 24 per cent by sons or daughters. This is not because spouses are inherently more violent, but because living with a spouse in later life is more common than living with adult children.

(ii) Older *men* were more likely to be abused than women, but primarily because they are more likely to be living with someone rather than alone and they are typically the older partner in a marriage or relationship and hence more frail. Abuse of men had not shown up in previous studies based on agency reports, partly because it was not as serious as abuse of women and hence less likely to be reported under adult abuse policies.

(iii) Another, unexpected, finding was that where people could not answer for themselves and carers were asked by proxy, they reported a higher rate of abuse than when older people were asked themselves. This seems to suggest carers are willing to acknowledge that they are at risk of abusing. But it also reflects the fact that older people who could not answer for themselves were likely to be among the most dependent and unwell: the household dynamics would be therefore under more pressure and be more likely to give rise to abuse.

This study did challenge my assumption about the most common form of elder abuse being that of an older woman by her daughter. You may remember that Corinne, Allan's colleague, also had this view quite firmly in her mind. She will need to acknowledge that most elder abuse is in fact spouse abuse, and that service provision needs to be developed to reflect that.

The other information which can be gleaned from this study is the *extent* of elder abuse. This will help Allan's social services department to plan ahead. Remember that extent of abuse can be expressed as a prevalence or an incidence rate. This study calculates both. It says that, for all types of abuse, between 25 and 39 people per 1,000 over 65 will have been abused – that is, about 3 per cent. This translates to an incidence – that is, the number of new cases coming to light each year – of 26 per 1,000. We can see that these cases have not all been reported; in Massachusetts, where the study was carried out, under the statute which makes it mandatory to report incidents of abuse, only 1.8 people per 1,000 were identified in the same period (about 1 in 14 of the actual cases). This leads Pillemer and Finkelhor to conclude that even with proper legislation, and mandatory reporting, 'substantial underreporting of elder abuse exists ... programs may be treating only a fraction of potential victims' (Offprints Book, p. 140). In other words, the kind of policy Allan is developing is likely to uncover only the tip of the iceberg: by no means will it reveal all the abuse which is perpetrated on older people in his department's catchment area.

Again, research can really inform practice through this kind of study. The authors attempted to reach older people themselves, so that they could get the most accurate picture of abuse as it affects *all* older people, not only those who have been in touch with service agencies. They found a predominance of spouse abuse which had largely been downplayed, not

> *... due to the less serious nature of this abuse but instead to the more ambiguous moral imagery that this problem conjures up.*

(*Offprints Book, p. 139*)

They were able to translate their findings into new suggestions for policy and service development, including a focus on:

1   educating professionals about the problem of spouse abuse

2   educating older people themselves about the issue of spouse abuse, and

3   developing services such as refuges and self-help groups for older women who have been abused.

From these studies you have learnt to read research findings critically, noting differences in definition, in populations, and in the way figures are presented as prevalence or incidence rates. You should now feel confident if you want to look at other areas of the literature – for example, you may want to review research on domestic violence (Dobash and Dobash, 1992), child protection (reviewed by Birchall, 1989), or other specific types of abuse, or people at risk.

Key points

- Research methods vary and yield different rates of abuse, which may be biased towards or against particular types or configurations of abuse.

- Sensitivity to service users is the key to high levels of reporting.

- The most inclusive information about abuse comes directly from people who have been victimised.

- A different picture will emerge from different levels in the service system as information is filtered out at each level.

- The picture of abuse gained from agency reports cannot be assumed to be an accurate mirror of *all* actual abuse.

- Research can suggest new avenues and priorities for service development.

Section 5
Prevention

After several days, Allan stopped reading and scratched his head. He had a clear framework in his mind about how abuse should be identified, investigated and monitored, but also some questions about whether this should be the only, or even the main, focus. After a cup of coffee he began to wonder if this wasn't just the meat in the sandwich because the policy, as he had so far conceived it, would do nothing to prevent abuse occurring, nor would it create any support systems to actually *help* people who have been abused. He wrote three large headings:

- before

- during

- after

and realised he had only filled in the structures to deal with the middle block. He took a step back.

As the old adage goes, prevention is better than cure, but what practical steps can a social services department like Allan's take to minimise the risk of abuse in their services and in the community at large? There are issues not only of *when* to intervene and *how proactive* to be, but also a tough question to be faced about what influence the social services (or any other social welfare agency) can exert over the forces which lead to abusive situations. You saw in Unit 22 how care inevitably crosses boundaries and so risks becoming intrusive or oppressive. Also in Unit 23 you looked at some wider social inequalities, such as those between parents and children, men and women, different ethnic groups, managers and low-paid workers – all of which factors contribute to abuse.

Allan knows his department and his policy cannot change the world, so what can it change? Should the social services put its resources into prevention or into protection? Is a system which focuses on identification and investigation of abuse providing valuable redress or merely locking the stable door after the horse has bolted? This dilemma has been most clearly articulated in relation to child protection, where the issue of whether to put resources into family support as opposed to investigation was the focus of intense debate in the mid-1990s. The 1995 Dartington Social Research Unit report *Child Protection: Messages from Research*, which you came across in Unit 23, was part of a government-led initiative to revisit these choices. You may remember Bernice struggling with this dilemma too, wondering if she shouldn't just help Sue by giving her extra playgroup sessions as an alternative to reporting her concerns under the child protection procedures.

5.1 Intervening at different levels

Abuse prevention work would have to take in different spheres as well as different stages in the process. A number of researchers in this field have drawn up models which emphasise the different layers that create abusive situations – from wider social attitudes, structures of service provision and family relationships, interpersonal characteristics and beliefs through to individual behaviour and pathology. Sobsey (1994) terms this an 'ecological' model and visualises it as a series of concentric circles within which individual abuses are located (see overleaf).

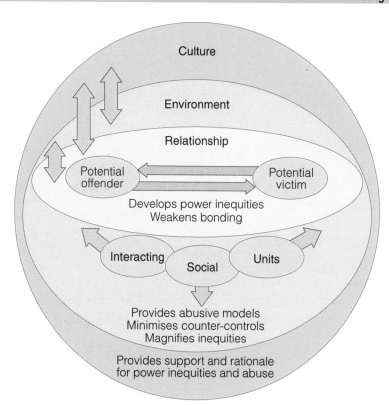

Figure 2
The integrated ecological model of abuse. Physical and psychological aspects of the interacting individuals are considered within the context of environmental and cultural factors (Sobsey, 1994, p. 160)

What extent of state input do you think is appropriate? Should it be comprehensive, in that social welfare agencies work *proactively* to develop communities and overcome inequalities, or *intermediate*, in that they intervene only on the basis of identified (and to some extent rationed) need, or *reactive*, in that they engage with people only as a last resort when abuse has been uncovered and damage limitation is unavoidable (Hardiker *et al.*, 1995)?

In the current climate resources and legislation tend to support only the latter two approaches. A social services department might be able to influence beliefs in the community at large about parenting, or attitudes to older people or people with disabilities, but its influence in these spheres is marginal. In its own residential homes, and in services with which it contracts, however, it has a clear responsibility and power to promote positive attitudes and safe practice. You have read about a number of approaches to prevention which could be undertaken within this fairly limited remit, including being clear about what constitutes abuse, setting boundaries around professional relationships, supporting service users and identifying abuse when service users do disclose or signal that they are in trouble.

Brown (1994) refers to these strategies for prevention as the five Ss:

State	define the nature and threshold of abuse clearly
Specify	clarify good practice and appropriate boundaries through guidance and training
Strengthen	empower potential victims through advocacy, education and support
Screen	scrutinise staff and volunteers and use rigorous recruitment practice
Stop	intervene to contain abuse once it has happened to protect individuals from serial or escalating abuse.

Recruitment is an issue Allan had not expected to feature in his policy. However, calls for better practice in recruitment were made in relation to children's services (see Department of Health, 1992) and taken up in relation to adult services (ARC/NAPSAC, 1993). This would include the need to:

- take up references
- conduct in-depth job interviews
- provide proper supervision, and
- avoid indiscriminate use of short-term agency staff.

You will read more about some of these issues of professional regulation in Block 7.

Sharp rise in nurses struck off shows tightening of discipline

Almost 90 nurses have been struck off the professional register in the past year, nursing leaders disclosed yesterday. Twelve have been removed for sexual misconduct.

The figures, which show a sharp rise in strikings-off, suggest the profession's regulatory body is taking a tougher line on discipline after being criticised for being too lenient.

(*Guardian*, 6 November 1996, p. 9)

Activity 10   Prioritising resources

Allow about 10 minutes   Suppose that Allan has been given a budget of £15,000 to support work on sexual abuse of adults with learning difficulties. He has the choice of spending it on:

- prevention, in the form of an excellent sex-education programme
- assessment and investigation, by training some designated senior care workers in investigative skills, or
- counselling services for people who have been abused.

How much of the budget would *you* apportion to meet need before, during or after abuse had taken place? You should be aware that this exercise is very hypothetical, not only because it is unlikely that this amount of money would be available, but also because resources often come in the form of people's time and expertise or attached to programmes. However, it is designed to help you think about where you would put your money, and to acknowledge that resource decisions are increasingly made in an 'either/or' climate.

Comment   I thought initially that I would want to allocate most of the resources to prevention (I apportioned about £8,000 for prevention, £5,000 for investigation and £2,000 for counselling). But once I had decided on this, I became concerned that maybe it would be pointless to investigate abuse and put a lot of energy into recognition if you have nothing further to offer. If counselling were more readily available, more people could be helped. I realised that I was also trying to juggle how effective I thought the measures to prevent or investigate abuse might be. Could I afford to skimp on counselling because I could hope to have reduced the overall level of abuse as a result of the other measures?

Key points

- Policies should address issues of service safety as part of their responsibility to prevent abuse.

- Agencies may have to decide whether to prioritise action to prevent, to identify and investigate, or to support people who have been abused.

- Stringent recruitment practice is necessary in services for children or vulnerable adults.

Section 6
Planning appropriate service provision

As you have seen, practice in the UK in relation to abuse of both children and vulnerable adults has so far developed through policies and procedures which highlight the intermediate stages: identification and investigation, as opposed to prevention and aftercare. This has also been the pattern in the USA. It tends to downplay the importance of remedial help for people once abuse has been brought into the open. The Dartington team concur with this assessment in relation to child protection work:

> *While there is good inter-agency co-operation at the point of assessing risk to a child, when it comes to delivering services, there is less sharing and a poor allocation of roles.*

> *(Dartington Social Research Unit, 1995, p. 36)*

They highlight the dearth of treatment options for either victims or perpetrators and their report was itself part of an explicit government initiative to shift resources away from investigative activity towards prevention and support.

6.1 What do people need?

Throughout this course you have been considering what are appropriate services for people with different needs at different times in their lives. The kind of planning Allan will need to do in developing services for people who have been abused is no different, in its nuts and bolts, from that in other schemes such as the Phoenix Centre, which you read about in Unit 18. He will need to make an assessment of what kind of support is most acceptable and most needed and then estimate how many people have need of such a service before looking at what agency or voluntary organisation is best placed to provide it.

Activity 11   **Options for service development**

Allow about 10 minutes   In this activity you are going to 'brainstorm' what kinds of services are needed by people who have been abused. Jot down your ideas on a sheet of paper. If you have trouble focusing your thoughts, think about:

- Darren and Tom, the two young men who were abused in Mr and Mrs D's residential home which was closed down (Unit 22, Section 2.4)
- Sue and her daughter (Unit 23, Section 2)
- Garry, Betty's son, whom you heard about on Audio Cassette 6, side 2
- Ken (this unit, Section 2.2).

What helped, or could have helped, them to recover?

You might also find some useful ideas in the last paragraph of Offprint 34, which you read for Activity 9.

Comment   I listed: one-to-one counselling; help lines; practical help with
             accommodation and money; a longer term men's or women's group; victim
             support groups; a refuge; rape crisis; self-help groups; art therapy. I
             thought that anyone going to court might need special help to prepare
             them for the experience and to support them through it. Did you have any
             other ideas?

             These services might step in to help people recover and to provide
             continued protection. Some provide time-limited help, such as with a court
             case or financial and accommodation worries, whereas others are longer
             term and more focused on sustaining personal recovery. Not everyone
             would be able to access mainstream services, such as victim support
             services or relationship counselling, without help, especially if they have
             additional special needs. Some people who already use services, such as
             Darren and Tom, would need help in the form of new placements (and
             support through a move, as you planned for in Unit 9). Other service users
             might be able to stay where they are, minimising any further disruption in
             their lives. But they may also need some changes, for example in who
             gives them intimate care, or who lives alongside them. A mixed ward, or
             group home, may not be appropriate for women who use services if they
             have been abused by men. Services need to take special care when they
             are making placements for service users who abuse others, as they have
             to balance their needs with those of other, possibly more vulnerable,
             service users (Brown and Thompson, 1997).

6.2 Specialist service provision

One of the issues Allan is considering is how far his authority needs to
provide (or support) specialist rather than generic services. Should they,
for example, set up a specialist shelter for older women who have been
affected by domestic violence, or ask their local refuge to extend its
services and make sure they are more alert to these needs? The council
could perhaps fund a specialist worker at a fraction of the cost of a
whole new service. Allan is challenged in his thinking by a paper
detailing how a specialist service for deaf and deaf-blind people was
developed in Seattle (Merkin and Smith, Offprint 35). You are going to
read this paper next to help you think through issues about planning,
and particularly about specialist service development. I learnt a lot that
was new to me about the deaf community, but I also found the stages
through which this agency went rang bells in relation to setting up
special service provision for people with learning difficulties.

There are also echoes in relation to service provision for people from
ethnic minorities, who share with deaf people their special needs
around language, culture and sometimes being members of a more
'closed' community. As the authors of the paper comment:

> *A hearing victim would probably choose a new circle of friends –*
> *something that is not always possible in our community.*

> *(Offprint 35, p. 149)*

**This is the telephone number
for Beverley Lewis House**

A Refuge for Women with Learning Disabilities

0181 - 522 0675

(Voice or Minicom)

P.O. BOX 7312
London E15 4TS

Powerhouse

In Partnership

EastThames

Community Care Department
East Thames Housing Group Limited

© Copyright 1996 Beverley Lewis House

The Beverley Lewis House
is a Safe House

for Women with learning disabilities who feel
frightened, or are being treated in a bad way

and want it to stop.

If you are being or have been attacked or
treated in a bad way

you can do something about it.

You can telephone Beverley Lewis House
and can speak to a woman worker

Do some groups need special services?

> **Study skills: Time pressures**
>
> You are reaching the end of a very full unit, in a very full block. How much time and energy do you have left for another reading? You might decide you just cannot afford the time, without falling behind the weekly schedule for the course. On the other hand, it *is* a very interesting paper. So perhaps you should at least read through it quickly, even if you don't have time to make notes. But then again, it may turn out to be the most valuable part of the unit for you, so that you decide to do the activity below in full and make up time somewhere else. You are facing choices that students everywhere face. What are you hoping to get out of the course? How much time can you give? Where are you going to invest your main efforts? It is up to you to take control of these decisions. Only you can judge your own needs and your own limits.

Activity 12   Developing a specialist service

Allow about 40 minutes

As you read Offprint 35, you might be able to see parallels with the special needs of a group of people you work with. I saw a lot of valuable links to the needs of women with learning difficulties. Use the questions below as a way of structuring your notes on the paper. If you work with people who have special needs, you may want to add some notes about similar needs in your group.

(a)   Why set up a specialist service for this group of people rather than including them within mainstream provision? What are their special needs and what barriers affect them particularly? (pp. 103–4 and p. 143)

(b)   How did this service get going? What triggered it off and how did it develop? (p. 144)

(c)   What services does the agency provide? (pp. 146–8)

(d)   What are the goals and target audiences of its educational initiatives? (pp. 149–51)

(e)   What did the agency do to make sure its services were accessible and 'user-friendly' (pp. 145–6)

(f)   How does the service know if it is being effective? (p. 151)

Comment   My notes look like this. You will see that I also did some thinking about services for women with learning difficulties. My notes on the article are labelled (i) and the notes relating to women with learning difficulties (ii).

(a)   Why a specialist service?

　　(i)   Problems of access
　　　　Specific cultural needs, including sensitivity to gender and body language.

　　(ii)   Women with learning difficulties also might need a service which offers help with communication and could address the stigma such women often experience relating to sexual issues
　　　　Legacy that they are not supposed to be sexual at all, or to enter into ordinary relationships – can translate into a 'told you so' attitude.

(b) How service got going

    (i) ADWAS service set up after brutal murder.

        One key innovator got group together – formed a voluntary association – grant from State Department – initially trained 12 volunteer advocates.

    (ii) Similar to the way an organisation called VOICE began in the UK, to support people with learning difficulties and their families when they had been sexually abused. Started by a parent whose daughter had been abused, who encountered barrier after barrier getting the case to court.

(c) What services does the agency provide?

    (i) The ADWAS service provides:

- 24-hour crisis line and help in taking a case right through to court
- counselling programme for deaf and deaf-blind children, a shelter and safe houses, individual and group counselling/ therapy
- court-ordered assessments and expert witness testimony in court.

    (ii) Women with learning difficulties might need all these things, also perhaps some extra sex education to compensate for lack of information available to them in this area of their lives. At present in UK these services are provided by different agencies. No 24-hour help line as yet.

(d) Goals and target audiences of educational initiatives

    (i) Educational programme targeted at different audiences.

        (I tried to jot down UK equivalent agencies.)

Types of audience	UK examples	Aim of programme
Deaf and deaf-blind people	Same	Information and consciousness raising to break the taboo, tailored to each group
Service providers	Social services; day centre and residential home managers; voluntary organisations; advice agencies	How to recognise abuse and when to refer
Organisations which may come into contact with deaf and deaf-blind people because of a sexual assault or domestic violence	Police; court officers; rape crisis; victim support; police doctors; Crown Prosecution Service; lawyers; judges; magistrates	'Deafness as a culture not pathology': how to deal with the person respectfully around the assault and not focus on the disability

    (ii) I found this a useful structure to look at in terms of women with learning difficulties. Opened up for me the importance of educating mainstream groups, emphasising 'debunking common myths'. Also found helpful the distinction between individual, systems and legal advocacy.

(e) Ensuring services are accessible and user-friendly
   (i) ADWAS:
   - made sure it was an agency run mainly by deaf people, with a majority of deaf people on the Board
   - made sure it used appropriate technology for receiving calls and referrals – all materials in Braille or large print.
   (ii) A service in London for women with learning difficulties also ensures materials are accessible and users are consulted.

(f) How does the service know if it is being effective?
   (i) ADWAS service has:
   - monitored its own cases
   - traced how at first abused deaf women were leaving hearing partners but are now also leaving partners who are deaf, indicating that 'people in the core of our community are facing the issue of violence in their lives'.

   Other measures of effectiveness would be more cases going to court; more direct referrals; more workshops to community groups.
   (ii) For women with learning difficulties many measures are similar – but there are more risks associated with service provision itself.

   I liked the measure of direct referrals – would indicate that women with learning difficulties had been given information which empowered them to take steps to keep themselves safe.

   Also the measure of increased court cases – would demonstrate that service had permeated mainstream professions and institutions on behalf of women with learning difficulties, who are currently not well served, especially by the criminal justice system.

Key points

- Services will probably need both informal community and formal state support (funding) to get going.

- Access issues are crucial in serving marginalised groups. Special attention needs to be paid to communication and culture.

- A wide range of services is needed to help vulnerable people in the aftermath of sexual or personal violence.

- Educational strategies need to be carefully targeted for vulnerable people themselves, specialist service providers and mainstream groups and institutions.

or you could ask a social worker or a friend to do it for you.

We can arrange to meet you about living in the Safe House.

You need Social Services to agree to pay for your place at the Safe House before you can move in.

You can stay at the Safe House until you find your own safe home (up to 2 years).

If you come and live in the Safe House

you will live with other women who have also been attacked, or who have been treated in a bad way.

You can be on your own when you want to.

There will be women workers who can help you learn to do more things for yourself, like:

Using money   Speaking up for yourself

We can find a woman counsellor who you will be able to talk to about your problems.

For the Safe House to be safe, the address has to be confidential. This means that you cannot tell your family or your friends where you are living.

Beverley Lewis House works to be fully accessible to women with physical/sensory disabilities.

Report of an Information Day on Elder Abuse

Appendix 2

Older People have the right to live in their own homes without the fear of harm from someone they know

But some older people live their life in constant fear of:

- Being hit
- Being bullied
- Being dominated
- Being kept hungry
- Being neglected
- Having their money or possessions misused or stolen.

If this is happening to you or someone you know you can do something now!

ⅲ Lewisham *Social Services*

Making information accessible

6.3 Interagency partnerships

Domestic violence tragedy triggers collaboration call

Professionals in the health, probation and social services fields need to ensure closer collaboration when dealing with people with histories of domestic violence and mental illness, an independent inquiry has concluded.

The inquiry was commissioned by Bromley Health Authority, the South East London Probation Service and the social services and housing department of the London Borough of Bromley after a man absconded from a probation hostel in Beckenham and murdered his estranged wife.

The inquiry concluded that a greater exchange of information between all the services involved in the case could have highlighted the risk.

'The geographical dispersion of the agencies involved makes it hard to be sure you have the full story, especially when you do not know the person's past history,' said Steve Catling, mental health commissioning manager at Bromley Health Authority.

The inquiry recommended the Department of Health and the Home Office issue joint guidance to all health authorities, social services departments and criminal justice authorities. This would be an update to the 1995 Home Office circular *Domestic Violence – Don't Stand For It*.

(*Community Care*, 5–11 June 1997)

In the previous section we considered the merits of specialist service provision; however, that is not, and cannot be, the whole story. Read the newspaper report above. Allan questioned right at the beginning the ambiguous exclusion of domestic violence from the vulnerable adults policy, and we have seen that such abuse is no respecter of client group status: as we have seen, elder abuse in particular is often a form of spouse abuse. Disabled people, people with learning difficulties and older people may be vulnerable to particular risks because they use services and are in receipt of residential or personal care, but they are also subjected to violence in their personal relationships, homes and communities because these are relatively 'ordinary' life experiences. A special focus on one group should not lead to insularity. Abuse must be considered in a wider context, and society-wide agencies, such as the police and criminal justice system, also need to change to become more responsive to *all* people who have been abused and seek redress. As the Seattle service says:

> ... *we do not work in isolation. We are a member of many coalitions and are active in local and state domestic violence and sexual assault committees. Each staff person at one time or another is ... committed to system change. Although we encourage referrals to our agency, we provide ongoing training with every domestic violence and sexual assault agency in the county so that these agencies are always prepared to serve Deaf and Deaf-Blind victims ... And because we all share common funding, we generally do lobbying as a group.* **The mutual support and respect we have for one another in the end helps victims** [my emphasis].

(*Merkin and Smith, Offprint 35, p. 146*)

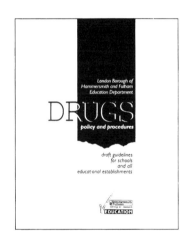

Working together ...

Allan is currently looking to develop an overarching policy for all 'vulnerable' adults – that is, for those adults who belong to groups entitled to receive social services because of special needs they have, over and above any abuse they suffer. But he does not want to isolate these groups from other sources of support and expertise.

When it comes to domestic violence, although vulnerable client groups are likely to be victims alongside others (mainly women) in the community, social services does not have the only remit; Allan is aware that when children are affected by domestic violence there may be disjunction between what is done under the aegis of child protection and what is done to protect adult women. A community-wide approach is going to be needed, and he can see that co-ordination at authority-wide level may be more appropriate, so that housing, the police, and the voluntary sector can be more coherently brought together.

Allan feels confident that he has researched the three parts of his brief:

- to think about what needs to be covered in policy and procedures on abuse of vulnerable adults
- to report back to the department on the incidence of adult abuse and what the common patterns are
- to put forward a plan for service development in partnership with other agencies.

He has been inspired by the ADWAS service, and has come to share their belief that:

> ... *violence is a learned behaviour and must not be tolerated ... [Society] provides a constant barrage of violent images, but only a limited amount of information to contradict such violence*

and their commitment to:

> ... *work tirelessly to ensure that non-violence can take root and thrive in our culture.*

> (*Offprint 35, p. 151*)

He has decided to put that quote at the beginning of his policy document, to remind people what they are doing it all for.

As you settle down to write your next TMA, Allan will be compiling his report to the departmental management team. You might like to think about who has the easier task!

Conclusion

In this unit we have covered some key issues about the role of policy and service development. Allan started out by focusing on the needs of people who were vulnerable in some 'labelled' way, but moved on to consider abuse within a wider context and make links with work in child protection and domestic violence across the whole community.

These were the core questions addressed in this unit, together with some key ideas you have covered:

How can policies and procedures help in abusive situations and relationships?

- Policies can set out the aspirations a service or agency may have to prevent, recognise and respond to abuse of children or vulnerable adults, and procedures translate policies into clear instructions about who should do what.

- Policies can alert people to the nature and patterns of abuse and abusing.

- Policies need to balance the needs of workers for guidance and those of managers for structures to assure accountability.

What can be learnt from accounts by users, practitioners and whistle-blowers?

- First-hand accounts demonstrate the impact of abuse over many years and also the barriers that exist to disclosing and being believed.

- Individual accounts need to be placed in context by referring to quantitative studies, so it can be seen how typical they are.

- Even unusual cases are a good test of how the system works.

What is the scale of the problem?

- Estimates vary depending on where information is drawn from.

- The extent of abuse may be expressed in terms of prevalence (the proportion of people abused in a given population) and incidence (the number of new cases within a given catchment area).

- Finkelhor and Pillemer estimate that about 3 per cent of older people are abused.

- A range of studies suggests that approximately one-half of all women with learning difficulties and one-quarter of men are sexually abused at some time in their lives, but services only identify a fraction of this.

What can we learn from research?

- Individual accounts show how abuse is experienced by vulnerable people and what service response they have encountered.

- Large-scale surveys reveal patterns and help to determine the extent of abuse within a given population.

- Figures collated from services can help agencies to evaluate their effectiveness in recognising and responding to abuse.

How can abuse be prevented?

- Prevention can focus on wider inequalities, safe services or relationship issues.

- Specifying good practice and clear professional boundaries helps to keep people safe when using services.

- Stepping in once abuse has been recognised can prevent repeated or escalating abuse.

What do people who have been abused need to help them recover?

- People need a wide range of service provision and also access to self-help groups and specialised services.
- They may also need some changes in their usual day and residential services to help them feel safe.

How can appropriate services and interagency partnerships be developed?

- Identifying need, mobilising commitment within the community and obtaining funding are key factors in setting up a service.

Conclusion to the block

In this block you have seen how people in residential care might be isolated, out of sight and out of mind, but that the staff who work with them might also be exploited and insecure as workers and potential advocates for them. Within the wider community you saw how difficult it is for concerned people to step across usual boundaries in order to protect children or adults, and how wider issues such as racism, poverty and attitudes towards gender and family relationships might provide a backdrop which allows abuse to flourish. Empowering people to act *for* themselves and *against* abusers requires community-wide support and policing. At its worst, abuse involves fear and terror, making personal safety a critical issue and a quality indicator within services. Acting against abuse at an individual level needs to be mirrored in action to address inequality within the community at large and within service structures and provision specifically.

Explicit policies set up mandatory procedures and create systems which make abusing difficult and reporting of abuse easier: this gives out a strong signal to potential abusers which assures them that where abuse does occur it will be picked up and acted upon accordingly. Service workers very clearly have a duty to protect as well as to empower, and the structures we have spelt out in this block show how they can work together to do this.

In Unit 25 you will have an opportunity to practise some of the skills which have been highlighted in this block.

References

ARC/NAPSAC (1993) *It Could Never Happen Here!: The Prevention and Treatment of Sexual Abuse of Adults with Learning Disabilities in Residential Settings*, ARC/NAPSAC, Chesterfield/Nottingham.

Bennett, E. (1996) 'Can you hear me?' in Malone, C., Farthing, L. and Marce, L. (eds) *The Memory Bird: Survivors of Sexual Abuse*, Virago, London, pp. 121–8.

Bennett, G. and Kingston, P. (1993) *Elder Abuse: Concepts, Theories and Interventions*, Chapman and Hall, London.

Birchall, E. (1989) 'The frequency of child abuse – what do we really know?' in Stevenson, O. (ed.) *Child Abuse: Public Policy and Professional Practice*, Harvester Wheatsheaf, Brighton.

Brown, H. (1994) 'Lost in the system: acknowledging the sexual abuse of adults with learning disabilities', *Care in Place*, Vol. 1, No. 2, pp. 145–57.

Brown, H. and Stein, J. (eds) (1996) *But Now They've Got a Voice: A Tape About Sexual Abuse for Service Users Made by Service Users*, Pavilion Publishing, Brighton.

Brown, H. and Stein, J. (1997) *Implementing Adult Protection Policies in Kent and East Sussex*, interim report available from School of Health and Social Welfare, Open University.

Brown, H., Stein, J. and Turk, V. (1995) 'The sexual abuse of adults with learning disabilities: report of a second two year incidence survey', *Mental Handicap Research*, Vol. 8, No. 1, pp. 3–24.

Brown, H. and Thompson, D. (1997) 'Service responses to men with learning disabilities who have sexually abusive or unacceptable behaviours: the case against inaction', *Journal of Applied Research in Intellectual Disability*, Vol. 10, No. 2, pp. 176–97.

Brown, H. and Turk, V. (1992) 'Defining sexual abuse as it affects adults with learning disabilities', *Mental Handicap*, Vol. 20, No. 2, pp. 44–55.

Buchanan, A.H. and Wilkins, R. (1991) 'Sexual abuse of the mentally handicapped: Difficulties in establishing prevalence', *Psychiatric Bulletin*, Vol. 15, pp. 601–5.

Churchill, J., Brown, H., Horrocks, C. and Craft, A. (1997) *There Are No Easy Answers: Service Responses to People With Learning Disabilities Who Sexually Abuse Others*, ARC/NAPSAC, Chesterfield, Nottingham.

Cooke, L.B. (1990) 'Abuse of mentally handicapped adults', *Psychiatric Bulletin*, Vol. 14, pp. 608–9.

Dartington Social Research Unit (1995) *Child Protection: Messages from Research*, HMSO, London.

Department of Health (1992) *Choosing with Care: The Report of the Committee of Inquiry into the Selection, Development and Management of Staff in Children's Homes* (The Warner Report), HMSO, London.

Dobash, R. and Dobash, R. (1992) *Women, Violence and Social Change*, Routledge, London.

Dunne, T.P. and Power, A. (1990) 'Sexual abuse and mental handicap: preliminary findings of a community-based study', *Mental Handicap Research*, Vol. 3, No. 2, pp. 111–25.

Glaser, B. and Strauss, A. (1967) *The Discovery of Grounded Theory: Strategies for Qualitative Research*, Aldine, New York.

Hard, S. and Plumb, W. (1987) 'Sexual abuse of persons with developmental disabilities: a case study', unpublished manuscript.

Hardiker, P., Exton, K. and Barker, M. (1995) *The Prevention of Child Abuse: A Framework for Analysing Services*, NSPCC, London.

Home Office in conjunction with the Department of Health (1992) *Memorandum of Good Practice: Video Recorded Interviews with Child Witnesses for Criminal Proceedings*, HMSO, London.

Malone, C., Farthing, L. and Marce, L. (eds) (1996) *The Memory Bird: Survivors of Sexual Abuse*, Virago, London.

McCarthy, M. and Thompson, D. (1997) 'A prevalence study of sexual abuse of adults with intellectual disabilities referred for sex education', *Journal of Applied Research in Intellectual Disability*, Vol. 10, No. 2, pp. 105–25.

Means, R. and Smith, R. (1994) *Community Care Policy and Practice*, Macmillan, London.

Overton, J. (1993) 'Child abuse, corporal punishment, and the question of discipline: the case of Mount Cashel', *Critical Social Policy*, Vol. 12, No. 3, pp. 73–95.

Pilgrim, D. (1995) 'Explaining abuse and inadequate care', in Hunt, G. (ed.) *Whistleblowing in the Health Service: Accountability, Law and Professional Practice*, Edward Arnold, London, pp. 77–89.

Pillemer, K. and Finkelhor, D. (1988) 'The prevalence of elder abuse: a random sample survey', *The Gerontologist*, Vol. 28, No. 1, pp. 51–7.

Reichardt, C.S. and Cook, T.D. (1979) 'Beyond qualitative versus quantitative methods', in Cook, T.D. and Reichardt, C.S. (eds) *Qualitative and Quantitative Method in Evaluation Research*, Sage, Beverly Hills.

Rose, S., Peabody, C. and Stratigeas, B. (1991) 'Undetected abuse amongst intensive case management clients', *Hospital and Community Psychiatry*, Vol. 42, No. 5, pp. 499–503.

Sobsey, R. (1994) *Violence and Abuse in the Lives of People with Disabilities*, Paul H. Brookes, Baltimore.

Stein, J. and Brown, H. (eds) (1996) *A Nightmare ... That I Thought Would Never End: A Tape About Sexual Abuse for Staff Made by Service Users*, Pavilion Publishing, Brighton.

Stevenson, O. (1996) *Elder Protection in the Community: What Can We Learn from Child Protection?*, Age Concern, King's College, London.

Turk, V. and Brown, H. (1993) 'The sexual abuse of adults with learning disabilities: results of a two year incidence survey', *Mental Handicap Research*, Vol. 6, No. 3, p. 196.

Wakefield, H. and Underwager, R. (1988) *Accusations of Child Sexual Abuse*, Thomas Springfield, Illinois.

Wardaugh, J. and Wilding, P. (1993) 'Towards an explanation of the corruption of care', *Critical Social Policy*, No. 37, Summer, pp. 4–31.

Williams, J., Watson, G., Smith, H., Copperman, J. and Wood, D. (1993) *Purchasing Effective Mental Health Services for Women: A Framework for Action*, Tizard Centre, University of Kent, Canterbury.

Yuille, J. (1988) (ed.) *Credibility Assessment*, Kluwer, Dordrecht.

Acknowledgements

Grateful acknowledgement is made to the following sources for permission to reproduce material in this unit:

Text

Brindle, D. 1996, 'Sharp rise in nurses struck off shows tightening of discipline', *The Guardian*, 6 November 1996, © *The Guardian*; 'Domestic violence tragedy triggers collaboration call', *Community Care*, 5–11 June 1997, published by permission of the editor of *Community Care*.

Figures

Figure 1: Turk, V. and Brown, H., 1993, 'The sexual abuse of adults with learning disabilities: results of a two year incidence survey', *Mental Handicap Research*, 6(3), © 1993 V. Turk and H. Brown, IBMH Publications; Figure 2: Sobsey, D., 1994, *Violence and Abuse in the Lives of People with Disabilities: The end of silence and acceptance?*, © 1994 Paul H. Brookes Publishing Company. All rights reserved.

Illustrations

P. 124: Melanie Friend/Format; p. 129: Stein, J. and Brown, H. (eds) *A Nightmare I Thought Would Never End*, Pavilion, in association with the Tizard Centre at the University of Kent; p. 133: Malone, C., Farthing, L. and Marce, L., 1996, *The Memory Bird*, cover by Janine Guice, Virago Press, Little, Brown and Company (UK); p. 140: Courtesy of Public Concern at Work, London; p. 142: *Community Care*, 10–16 July 1997, cover by Andrew Kingham, by permission of The Inkshed; pp. 167 (top) and 171 (top): User Leaflet for Beverley Lewis House, 1996, East Thames Housing Group; p. 167 (bottom left): courtesy of PowerHouse and Beverley Lewis House Refuge, East Thames Housing Group; pp. 167 (bottom middle left) and 171 (bottom): Lewisham Older Women's Network and The S.A.V.E. Project 1996, Informing Ourselves... So that we can empower others, Lewisham Social Services; p. 167 (bottom middle right): Voice UK – One Aim. One Voice. Voice UK, telephone 01332 519872; p. 167 (bottom right): Elder Abuse Response, Action on Elder Abuse; p. 173: Chipping, P. 1994, 'Community safety nationally...', Safety Matters – Community Safety Bulletin, Community Safety Unit, London Borough of Hammersmith and Fulham.

Unit 25
Managing Boundaries and Risk

Prepared for the course team by Hilary Brown

With thanks to Jan Walmsley for editorial comments and to Anthea Sperlinger for input on 'difficult behaviour'

While you are working on Unit 25, you will need:
- Course Reader
- *The Good Study Guide*
- Pathways VQ Guide
- Audio Cassette 6, side 1, part 1
- Skills video

Contents

Introduction

This is the last of the K100 'skills units'. In this unit we will be continuing to develop your practice skills by helping you to:

- put difficult areas of caring work into words in a way which allows them to be more openly acknowledged and addressed

- reflect on your role and the extent (and limits) of your responsibilities

- acknowledge how generic skills, such as assessment and planning, can help in situations where people have been, or are at risk of being, abused.

In the context of the issues dealt with in this block, we shall be reviewing two key areas:

- how to manage boundaries

- how to manage risk in situations where children or vulnerable adults might have been abused.

Throughout the course you have been considering some of the principles which should underpin good practice in social care: the values base. Previous skills units have helped you to get to grips with practice through observation and rehearsing specific study skills such as working with numbers or writing reports. In this unit we will be bringing together a number of the skills and insights you have been developing to see how you can apply your knowledge in the difficult and sometimes ambiguous situations which we have been exploring in Block 6.

Unit 25 focuses on:

- managing boundaries

- managing risk in situations where abuse is suspected

- reading graphs

- gearing up to revision

- developing writing skills.

You have seen that although everyone hopes that abuse doesn't 'happen here' in their service, neighbourhood or family, it is wise to be alert to the fact that it *can* happen anywhere. Prevention often hinges on having structures in place which guarantee openness and advocacy for more vulnerable people while also safeguarding their privacy and right to confidentiality: a difficult balance to achieve. It is often as important to think about *how* a decision should be made as *what* it should be and to have a clear view of what one is hoping to achieve for the person(s) concerned.

Block 6 has focused on dilemmas about what is private in public settings and what is of public concern in private settings. We have shown throughout the course that care relationships do not just happen 'naturally', they are shaped by economic and social factors which combine to create a situation in which women tend to take on informal care roles and gravitate into low paid care jobs. You have learnt how gender, race and poverty interact with the more formal aspects of hierarchy and that less powerful staff in residential settings often feel almost as powerless as service users. You have also seen how, in community settings, people like Bernice are often in a double bind: if they take action they risk being perceived as interfering, whereas if they stand by while someone comes to harm they may be held responsible. (Ruth, who you will meet on the skills video, also finds herself in this difficult situation.)

In exploring some of these dilemmas, Block 6 has covered a wide range of different types of 'underpinning' knowledge:

- knowledge about *behaviour*, how it is learnt, what purpose it serves and how to assess it (as we learnt in relation to Rosalie)

- knowledge about *regimes* and dynamics in residential care

- knowledge gained from debates on *values*, and the place of scientific evidence in such arguments

- knowledge about *ideologies* (systems of belief like the ones revealed in the songs you listened to on the tape), which mask unequal power and social or material inequalities behind assumptions about what is normal or natural

- knowledge gained from *first hand accounts*, by listening to survivors who have come through difficult situations or people who have tried to bring concerns about wrongdoing into the open

- knowledge about different kinds of *research* and how it links into public and professional awareness

- knowledge about service *planning*, service development and organisations.

Balancing acts

Because abuse is so complex this unit does not focus on any one area of values in isolation but looks at how they must all be held in balance. Abuse is not a *separate* area of work, neatly cordoned off from other aspects of day-to-day practice. Nor is it work which demands a completely different approach. It is a set of situations in which these approaches are put to the test. Abusive situations and relationships often challenge what we assume to be good practice and make it necessary to balance one principle against another: for example, the need to respect confidentiality has to be set against the need to share information in order to protect someone from harm.

The five principles of good practice which we have emphasised throughout the course are to:

- enable people to develop their own potential

- enable people to have a voice and be heard

- respect people's beliefs and preferences

- promote and support people's rights to appropriate services

- respect people's privacy and rights to confidentiality.

Each has a particular relevance to situations in which abuse is suspected. They will help to define situations where people are not being respected. They will also act as a guide in seeking appropriate support and redress for people who have been harmed.

You will, however, find that conflicts arise, such as between principles of:

- confidentiality and openness

- independence and protection

- control and freedom, and

- autonomy and intervention.

And don't think that if you don't get involved then the vulnerable child or adult will be automatically empowered. It isn't a case of minimum intervention equals maximum autonomy. It might be the opposite in cases where someone's autonomy is being undermined by a more powerful other. It might be that your intervention is the only thing which can guarantee the person's safety and autonomy.

Respect for individuals and the choices they have made is central – but so is acknowledgement of intimidation or coercion, which may make it look from the outside as if someone is colluding with an abuser or 'choosing to be abused' when actually they have few options. We saw that where individuals lack capacity to consent, their apparent agreement to sexual acts or financial transactions should not be accepted without scrutiny, and also that where people are economically or socially marginalised, their options may be limited.

You will also inevitably be faced with conflicts of interest, between victim and perpetrator, parent and child, staff and clients, and sometimes between fellow service users whose needs may not always be compatible.

You'll see some of these conflicts on the video, which introduces a character that you might recognise if you are keen on TV 'soaps'. Ruth from 'EastEnders' works in an after-school club. Her concerns about the possibility of abuse involving one of the boys who attends the club lead her into a series of dilemmas. These have a lot in common with those faced by Marie, Bernice and Adrian.

Unit 25 video content

Video Scene 10 'Managing risk: EastEnders' consists of 10 extracts from the BBC soap 'EastEnders'. It covers:

- being alert to signs of possible abuse and recording any concerns

- deciding what is abuse and what is proper discipline

- assessing difficult behaviour and its causes

- knowing who to get support from and when

- passing on concerns through officially recognised channels.

The sequences are as follows:

10(a) Ruth notices bruises on Adam's arm

10(b) Ruth talks to Mark about what is normal

10(c) Adam misbehaves again (view twice, the second time as an exercise in observation)

10(d) Ruth confronts Adam again

10(e) Ruth talks to Adam's mother

10(f) Ruth wonders what to do

10(g) Ruth talks to Tom, her senior worker

10(h) Ruth decides to talk to a social worker

10(i) Ruth questions Adam: does she go too far?

10(j) The story ends.

Working within the VQ framework

If you are interested in taking a Vocational Qualification (VQ) in Care at level 3 or 4 you will find that much of the work you do in this unit will be useful. First you will find that many of the generic skills you have learnt, such as assessing and planning for individuals or making accurate case notes, are going to be useful in relation to people who are facing abuse in their lives. But conversely you will also find that the specific focus of this block on potentially abusive situations can help you to sharpen your practice skills in more routine situations.

Competences such as:

- assessing and managing aggressive or abusive behaviours
- supporting clients in difficult relationships
- minimising the level of abuse in care environments
- contributing to the protection of individuals
- service planning to meet identified needs

are all covered in this unit. If you are employed in a care setting you will be in a good position to present clear examples for your portfolio. To help you see the close connection between the learning you'll do in Unit 25 and the VQ, you'll see an extract from the VQ Unit SC17 'Evaluate risk of harm, abuse and failure to protect' (level 4) in the box below, current at the time of writing (1998).

SC17. Evaluate risk of harm, abuse and failure to protect

Element
SC17.1 Identify potential risk of harm, abuse and failure to protect

Performance Criteria
SC17.1.1 Comprehensive information concerning clients' condition and behaviour is collected and checked for accuracy. *(Oe1)*

SC17.1.2 The purpose of the collection and compilation of information is accurately explained to relevant people/ agencies in a manner appropriate to their needs and understanding. *(Oe2)*

SC17.1.3 Directly observed evidence, reliable information, opinion and prejudice are accurately and clearly distinguished.

SC17.1.4 Factors which suggest that clients are at risk are correctly identified from best available information.

SC17.1.5 Information as to the existence of risk to clients is communicated to other colleagues using agreed dissemination procedures. *(Ob3)*

SC17.1.6 The limitations of the worker's role are strictly adhered to.

SC17.1.7 All records are comprehensive, accurate, up-to-date and kept in accordance with national and organisational guidelines. *(Ob7, 0, 10)*

Range Statements

(a) *Level of risk:* high; low.

(b) *Type of risk:* physical; sexual; emotional.

(c) *Condition and behaviour:* immediate; over time.

(d) *Relevant people and agencies:* those in the social network; other workers; other agencies.

All these competences rely on you sharing responsibility appropriately and not working in isolation or making decisions behind closed doors. Each will rely on:

- accurate recording

- prompt reporting of concerns

- careful and accurate collation of evidence, and

- formal, as opposed to informal, consultation and decision making.

 For further information on mapping to VQs see the Pathways VQ Guide which accompanies the course.

Key points

- The focus of this unit is on managing boundaries and making difficult decisions.

- Practice skills centre on record keeping and consultation in the context of risk.

- All the practice values are important even when these lead to conflicts or dilemmas.

Section 1
Managing boundaries

1.1 Being 'professional'

 In Unit 22 you heard from Vicky Golding about Enfield's work in developing guidelines on professional boundaries. You might want to listen to this part of Audio Cassette 6 again (side 1, part 1) to remind yourself about the areas which were covered in these guidelines and some of the controversies arising from this approach. One problem identified was how much personal information a worker should disclose to a client. Vicky Golding talked about the impact of something as common as having a picture of your family on your desk and the inequalities which might be involved in, for example, allowing someone to reveal their marital status but not the fact that they are gay or lesbian. Because boundaries are crossed in care work there is a need for them to be spelt out and sometimes to be restated in the daily interactions between service workers and users, carers and cared for. Activity 1 gives you the opportunity to consider some of these dilemmas in setting boundaries.

Activity 1   **Acceptable boundaries**

Allow about 10 minutes   Read the following extract and then answer the questions below.

> *Gerald, a man with moderate learning disabilities, had recently moved from a hospital setting to a group home. After a few months, staff asked for help in managing Gerald's 'aggressive outbursts'. On one occasion he had broken the windscreen wipers on a visitor's car, on another he had smashed the same car's headlights. He had also pulled his key worker's hair and threatened to punch her when she remonstrated with him for giving her a bone crushing hug.*
>
> *On investigation it transpired that Gerald, coming from a male hospital ward with male staff, was convinced that his female key worker's enthusiastic involvement in his progress and well-being was a sign of sexual interest. This misapprehension had been fostered unthinkingly by other members of staff, who at first jokingly agreed with Gerald when he referred to his key worker as his 'girlfriend', then actively promoted this by teasing remarks such as 'poor Gerald, your girlfriend's not here today'.*
>
> *Gerald's key worker was inexperienced. She had not challenged Gerald's early references to her as 'my girlfriend'. As she said, 'I didn't think there was any harm in it, and he looked so pleased to see me I didn't want to spoil the relationship I was building with him'. Similarly, although she later commented that Gerald's physical approaches increasingly made her feel uncomfortable, she had not objected at first because she knew how emotionally impoverished his life in the hospital had been. The damaged car belonged to the key worker's boyfriend, understandably seen by Gerald as a rival for her affection.*
>
> *Gerald, with few models to draw upon, was for a time confirmed in his beliefs by the explicit validation and repetition of his verbal claims, and by the acceptance of physical touch. Staff chose to amuse themselves with what they saw as 'only harmless teasing';*

Gerald's key worker allowed her boundaries of personal space to be invaded on the mistaken assumption that she was somehow compensating for past deprivation, and that this and the joking remarks were justifiable because they increased the rapport she needed to establish herself as a good key worker.

While members of staff and the key worker were all clear in their own minds where the boundaries lay – that Gerald was not, and would never be, her boyfriend – Gerald had no means of knowing this. The seemingly abrupt volte-face by his key worker and the disapproval of other staff when their limits of tolerance were reached confused and upset Gerald. It required careful reappraisal on everyone's part to arrive at acceptable boundaries of language and touch. Gerald paid an unacceptably high price in terms of his mental health, his self-esteem and self-confidence.

(Craft and Brown, 1994, pp. 4–5)

This extract mentions 'acceptable boundaries of language and touch':

(a) How could Gerald have been introduced to these boundaries more successfully?

(b) Are 'acceptable boundaries' different in another setting you are familiar with? If so, what are the differences?

Comment (a) We know that Gerald had moved from an all male environment, so we might have anticipated that he would have a lot of learning to do about how to relate to women (particularly young women). The service might have started off being more formal with him to help him establish boundaries – then relaxed when everyone felt comfortable that he could manage them (rather than start off too informal and then have to back off). What did you think?

(b) You came across another setting back in Unit 3, involving Lynne and a relationship with a male home carer (one we made up). There the boundaries were different because Lynne lived in a family home, held down a job and had a boyfriend. It is always important to consider what the norms around touching and use of language are – for example when you are working in someone's own home, or in a situation where you have to give intimate care – and for different groups of people – for example, older people, or people from different ethnic backgrounds.

Well thought out guidance helps workers to draw an appropriate line for themselves. It also assists managers by giving a reference point to use in supervising staff. (Remember the Enfield guidelines, which Vicky Golding says provide a useful tool for management, as well as for staff and users.) As in Gerald's case, it is not only language which can confuse boundaries. For example, services for people with learning difficulties have sometimes encouraged staff to bring their partners or children into work, with the idea that these contacts will help the service users learn to integrate themselves into community networks. This means that staff are being asked to use their personal contacts and lives as a way of creating 'normal relationships', while at the same time maintaining proper professional boundaries.

Activity 2   Helping staff to get the balance right

Allow about 10 minutes   We have seen at several points in the block that written guidance can be a helpful way of containing the contradictions built into staff roles. Write about half a page of 'rules', either for Gerald's service, or for a service setting you know, to address:

- teasing
- hugging
- staff bringing their partners into the conversation
- staff involving their partners in the service's activities or holidays.

Comment   Did your rules treat the kind of teasing which went on with Gerald as a sign of warmth or of insensitivity? Did you make allowance for staff to hug service users? Would you have let Gerald know that his key worker had a boyfriend? Would your rules allow/encourage her to involve her boyfriend if she was taking service users out for a social evening? Or would you see it as parading her good fortune in front of Gerald, who does not, at this stage, have the skills to find a partner? Did your rules take any account of whether services users had previously been in hospital environments? Did you come down on the side of 'inclusion' or 'professional distance' in terms of staff revealing details of their private lives, or taking clients into their own homes? How did you balance the need for people in residential settings to give and receive physical and verbal expressions of affection, against the dangers of giving misleading signals? If a home is run by a husband and wife team, is the line between marital and professional relationships even harder for residents and staff to negotiate? Does this require special rules?

Section 2
Managing risk

You saw in Unit 23 that as well as managing and crossing boundaries, care workers also have to manage risk and anxiety about the work they do. They are often faced with ambiguous situations, as Bernice was in relation to Sue and her daughter. They may not have enough information or evidence to act on their concerns about individuals or families with whom they are in contact. Child and adult protection procedures help workers to contain this anxiety by clarifying what they should do and mandating them to share their concerns with their own agency and other agencies such as the police or social services. The lead agency for the protection of children and vulnerable adults is social services, so concerns which persist should be formally investigated or taken forward by them. The video-based activities which follow will help you develop confidence in managing the risk inherent in such situations.

2.1 Using the video

The video clips you are about to view are based on the BBC programme 'EastEnders'. They outline a developing situation in which Ruth, who works in an after-school club in Walford, becomes concerned about a boy called Adam. You will see that she faces a number of dilemmas and sorts them out in a rather *ad hoc* way. She has obviously not received good child protection training and neither has her manager, nor her friend the social worker, whom she calls in. It is evident that none of them have studied K100! So, don't take their actions as 'good practice' but as a basis for addressing the issues yourself. We are going to deal with Ruth's concerns in two parts, focusing first on recording and assessment and second on the need for appropriate consultation.

As you work through each of the 10 sequences you will meet activities. In writing your responses you will be making the kind of record which could be used as evidence if a case like this were to be dealt with formally under child or adult protection procedures. By the time you have completed all the activities you will have an impressive dossier of evidence of your competence in observation and assessment of risk, and of your ability to make use of guidelines in potentially serious situations such as this.

As you work through the activities you will also find two forms or 'job aids' which you could adapt for use in your own service. One is for recording and assessing difficult behaviour and the other is to help you map the avenues open to you if you are concerned about potential abuse.

Instructions for viewing

Now it's time to set to work. It will be better if you do *not* watch all of the Scene 10 extracts in one go, but sequence by sequence, as you would if you were really involved, undertaking each activity as you go.

2.2 Recording and assessment

As you saw in the case study about Bernice, it can be very difficult to be sure what is going on in private relationships, such as those between parents and children. If someone is being harmed an outsider will only get occasional glimpses of the problems and will have to make a judgment based on fragments of information. A picture has to be put together from signs such as bruises, difficult behaviour, disclosures or isolated incidents. Once a worker has an idea that a child or vulnerable adult may be at risk they also have to make a judgment about whether it is serious enough to warrant action. Ruth has to balance both of these uncertainties: she does not know *if* Adam is being abused and *how serious* it might be if this proves to be the case. She is unclear about what she means by abuse and revisits the issues about discipline which you considered in Unit 23.

View each scene and address each of the associated activities.

Activity 3

Allow about 5 minutes

Noting signs which might give cause for concern

View scene 10(a) of the video. In this scene Ruth notices bruises on Adam's arm and asks him how they occurred.

This is the first indication Ruth has that all is not well with Adam. Imagine you are Ruth, write a note for Adam's file about the bruises – a few lines will do but make sure you have noted where the bruises are, how you saw them, what questions you asked and what he said about them. Try to report the exchange you had with Adam using your own, and his own, words.

As a matter of information, bruises of different ages/colouring might signal a series of injuries rather than one fall or bump. Also if injuries are evident in soft tissue parts of the body such as the neck, underarms, stomach, genitals or inner thighs these are unlikely to have occurred as a result of a fall or accident.

Comment My note for the file would include the following information:

- What was happening, i.e. I was calling him over for a story.

- What the bruises looked like and where exactly they were on his arm.

- That I had asked him about the 'marks on his arm' and he said 'Don't know'.

- That I asked if he could remember hurting his arm and he said 'No'.

- That I also asked him if the bruises still hurt and he said 'No'.

Activity 4 **Reference points**

Allow about 5 minutes View scene 10(b). Ruth is talking to Mark, her partner, in the pub about whether this is normal. Over the next few days she initiates a discussion with her friend Gita and further discussion with Mark about discipline and what is normal.

In scene 10(a) you saw that Adam's bruises triggered Ruth's concern. In the absence of any other concerns, how worried would you be by these bruises? Do you agree with Mark that being 'black and blue' is normal for a boisterous seven year old?

(a) On a scale of 1–10, where 10 is extremely worried and 1 is not at all worried, where would you stand?

1   10

|..|

(b) Where do you think Ruth has positioned herself?

1   10

|..|

Comment I think at this stage I would be less concerned than Ruth apparently is: I thought I might be a 6 and that Ruth had put herself as an 8. What did you think? I did think, however, that I would make a mental note to look out for bruises on Adam again.

This is a reprise of the debate on discipline in Unit 23. Remind yourself where you stand in relation to these issues. Are you with Gita who seems to be firmly against smacking or with Mark who doesn't think there is anything wrong with a 'clip around the ear'? Is hitting a child more serious than shouting? Ruth says her father 'had us so terrified we'd freeze at the sound of his voice'. Do you think there is a gender gap here?

If (and it is still unclear) Adam's bruises had been caused by being smacked or hit at home, do you think this would be 'abuse'? Would you think it was serious enough to do anything about it at this stage?

Activity 5   Describing Adam's behaviour

Allow about 5 minutes

View scene 10(c). It shows an incident between Ruth and Adam when he was painting. You will see Adam misbehaving again. Jot down a brief description of what happens as if you were Ruth putting a note on the file just before she goes home that evening.

Comment

You will remember that we looked at difficult behaviour in some detail in relation to Rosalie in Unit 22. Look back at Section 2 to remind yourself of some of the issues. Now look back at what you have written – what kinds of words have you used? Have you written that Adam was 'attention seeking' or just 'winding Ruth up' or did you use terms like 'challenging behaviour'?

Activity 6   Assessing Adam's behaviour using an *abc* chart

Allow about 15 minutes

Before you do this task you might want to revisit part 2, side 1 of Audio Cassette 6 where Anthea Sperlinger and Chad Botley discuss the general principles of assessment they applied to Rosalie's situation. Although they were considering difficult behaviour in the context of severe learning difficulties, what they say applies to everyone and might be useful here. They suggest using an *abc* chart as a framework for observation and you can practise using this in relation to Adam now. Look at the *abc* chart on the next page. See what you are being asked to record in detail to help work out the context and function of Adam's difficult behaviour.

Now rewind the video and watch scene 10(c) again. Observe exactly what happens. You will probably find you have to pause the video several times in order to concentrate on the exact sequence of events and use the blank *abc* chart (Job Aid 1 on page 196) to record your comments (you might want to copy it so you can use it again). You may notice more than one thing happening under each heading. Include *all* your ideas as they could provide valuable clues to Adam's difficulties.

When you have completed the observation briefly review what you have written. What do you think the trigger was? And the consequences?

Comment

My *abc* chart is on page 197. I could not see a clear cut 'cause' for Adam's behaviour from this one incident. I thought he might have disliked hearing his friend's work praised, or that he needed to get down from the table. Of course, if this were for real you would need to collect a lot of data to base your judgment on but what was your initial analysis?

Although there isn't a clear 'answer' in many situations like this I hope you found that this structured observation enabled you to begin a process of constructive assessment. This kind of approach can help to take the heat out of a situation, to remove some of the immediate emotional (and sometimes punitive) response and to gather information which will help everyone to analyse what is really going on.

2.3 Consultation

Ruth is clearly concerned about Adam and is having trouble controlling his behaviour. She still doesn't have enough information to know how best to deal with the situation. What should she do? As we saw in Units 23 and 24 the key to child or adult protection is appropriate and timely consultation, and much of the work which has been done to develop policy has focused on setting out channels for communication within social services and with other agencies. Sharing concerns and information is mandatory in the case of children and advisable in the case of vulnerable adults. We have seen that Ruth is working through a process of logging her concerns about Adam and trying to reach a judgment about whether to pass these on to anyone else or to another agency. She comes to a point where there is:

- enough evidence to warrant concern that Adam has problems, (bruises, difficult behaviour and demonstrating fear that he will be hit), and

- an awareness that if this were so it would be wrong not to intervene.

The next issue for Ruth is what she should do, having decided to act – to whom should she address her concerns. In the next series of video clips you will see how Ruth comes to a decision to take her concerns about Adam further and who she consults.

Activity 9   **Sharing concerns**

Allow about 5 minutes   View scene 10(f) in which Ruth is talking to Mark in the pub. He says 'Surely it can't be down to you to sort it out?' and he's right. Who should Ruth talk to first about her concerns?

Comment   I think she should share her worries with her manager in the first instance – what did you think? This is in fact what she does – she initiates a discussion with Tom, the senior worker at the after-school club.

Who would *you* share concerns with in your workplace or particular situation? Such a decision has a different feel to it if you are working within a formal structure such as Ruth's. If you were a concerned neighbour or relative you might find it more difficult to act if it involved contacting an agency like social services 'cold', without any prior contact with them.

Activity 10   **Sticking to your guns**

Allow about 10 minutes   View scene 10(g) in which Ruth talks to Tom, her senior worker.

Tom is not very helpful. When he says 'I don't see any evidence' and 'my sympathy is with his parents' he leaves Ruth, as a more junior member of staff, in an unenviable position.

What do you think he should have said and offered to do? Imagine he has a supervision session with Ruth. What advice could you offer him about how he should conduct the supervision session? List five 'pointers'.

1	
2	
3	
4	
5	

Comment It might have helped if he had made time to talk to Ruth in his office away from the children for a few minutes. I thought he should have:

1   listened to Ruth's concerns to find out the extent of her worries and the evidence she has observed; as it is, he dismisses them before he has heard what she has to say

2   asked her to keep a record of any injuries, hints or disclosures, or any further episodes of difficult behaviour

3   given her some concrete guidance on how to deal with Adam's behaviour if he is difficult with her again

4   told her what *not* to do, like not questioning Adam directly or gossiping to anyone

5   told her what kinds of things to look for which *would* give immediate rise to concern

6   agreed a date and time to jointly review the situation – this would ensure that Ruth is not left to shoulder the anxiety alone and give her a structure to work within, making it clear that he is taking responsibility as the senior worker.

As you saw in Unit 24, passing on concerns may not be enough. Adrian, the whistle-blower, found that a senior worker or manager may not immediately share your view. Their response might be as a result of greater experience but could also be because they do not appreciate the gravity of the situation – they might put your concern down to your inexperience or doubt the values you have drawn on in making your judgment.

Activity 11 **Making it official**

Allow about 5 minutes View scene 10(h) in which Ruth decides to contact her friend who is a social worker.

Rebuffed by her manager, Ruth is increasingly anxious about not sharing her concerns with someone more experienced. As Adrian in Unit 24 discovered, to take a complaint outside an establishment you have to know your way around the services and know 'what the next steps would be'. You have to know who you *can* and who you *should* go to. Ruth doesn't seem to have that local knowledge. We can only guess that she might be relatively new in the post and/or not have received proper induction training which would set out as a matter of course what channels to work through in the event of child protection concerns. So what you see in this clip is the result of her naivety and certainly not an example of good practice.

You will see that she and Mark (who is acting as her sounding board) are working on the basis of a number of misconceptions; see if you can jot them down as you watch the scene.

Comment   1   Ruth assumes that not being 'official' is important: she confuses the official nature of a report with the idea of Draconian action, perhaps influenced by the tabloid press who tend to sensationalise cases with talk of dawn raids accompanied by lurid details. She is expressing the same fear voiced by Bernice in Unit 23, that any action taken by social services would be more punitive than supportive. Mark echoes this by saying that social services would automatically create a 'mess'.

2   She seeks Nicola's help informally, outside the usual channels of communication within the framework of a local social services department, as if Nicola would or could act as a 'lone ranger' in relation to child protection issues. She says to Mark that Nicola is a 'professional', as if this would enable and allow her to seek out further information and reach an appropriate decision without recourse to anyone else. (You will learn more about what it means to be a professional in Block 7.) She assumes that Nicola is a free agent and could act outside official procedures when in fact she would be bound to log such a request for help and certain to make any further enquiries through appropriate channels. It might be, for example, that Adam and his family are already known to social services; their GP might have parallel concerns; maybe a member of Adam's household is known to the police. So while Nicola as an individual could act as a better informed sounding board than Mark, she would soon have to start acting within her professional *role* not simply on the basis of her own expertise or personal knowledge.

2.4 Clarifying roles

The legal position is that Ruth has a duty to report child protection concerns to her manager, and if he does not act on them, to social services directly. Under child protection procedures, all social services departments will consult in this kind of situation and it will be their decision when or whether to take action. So when Mark said to Ruth, 'it can't be down to you', he was quite right.

We have reprinted below Allan's notes about his (adult) protection policy (from Unit 24).

Allan's notes

The adult protection policy will identify who is responsible for the following tasks:

- **alerting:** that is, passing on a concern to a senior person either inside or, if necessary, outside the 'alerter's' own establishment or agency

- **reporting:** that is, making an official record of the alert and triggering action under the procedures

- **allocating the case:** that is, someone senior needs to decide what level of response is appropriate and which agency is best placed to lead the investigation

- **investigating:** that is, co-ordinating the gathering of information and the conduct of interviews, consulting other appropriate agencies to establish matters of fact and deciding how best to protect the vulnerable adult

- **decision making:** a case conference needs to be called to decide what to do next and who needs to know, to keep this person safe and protect others who might be at risk

- **monitoring:** means keeping track of individual cases, making decisions through case conferences and gathering information about adult protection work as a whole.

In this kind of structure Ruth's role is to be alert and pass on her concerns and that is all. Her manager, Tom, is responsible for bringing any concerns regarding the children at the after-school club to the *official* notice of the local social services department via a formal report (not a phone call to Ruth's friend).

Ruth did discharge her main responsibility which was to be alert to the risk of abuse and to pass on her concerns. This she did by telling Tom that she was worried about Adam, but since he does not take her concerns seriously she was left 'holding the baby'. So Ruth also needed a reserve, a back-up, who would pass these concerns on to the local social services department and initiate a preliminary check on existing information and perhaps a low-level intervention such as a brief chat with Adam's mother. It is Ruth's lack of knowledge about how to access this level of support which leads her to take matters into her own hands.

Activity 12   Overstepping the mark

Allow about 5 minutes

View scene 10(i) in which Ruth questions Adam, first through play and then directly, about more bruises.

What do you think of Ruth's actions?

In Unit 24, Section 2.4, Allan noted some official guidance on what workers should do if a child, or vulnerable adult, spontaneously discloses abuse to them in the course of play, or a routine interview or assessment.

Allan's notes

What to do if a child or vulnerable adult discloses an abusive relationship to you:

- listen rather than directly question

- never stop someone who is freely recalling significant events, in other words don't stop someone in full flow and say: 'Hold on, we'll come back to that later', as they may not tell you again

- at the first opportunity make a note of the discussion, which includes the time, the setting, anyone else there and exactly what was said in the person's own words

- date and sign the record.

(Guidance based on the Memorandum of Good Practice, Home Office in conjunction with the Department of Health, 1992, para. 1.8)

Did Ruth's interaction with Adam go beyond this?

Comment   Ruth has overstepped her role by quite a wide margin. She has directly questioned Adam, which is not the same as listening to any disclosure he might have offered himself, and she has bypassed the official route, breaching confidentiality as she does so – exactly the scenario which child protection structures are designed to avoid.

Activity 13   Clarifying your own role

Allow about 30 minutes   If you are employed in a care setting it is worth considering at this stage where *you* fit in. Look back at Allan's notes and fill in the names of the people in your service or setting who would carry out these responsibilities in Job Aid 2. Ask, if necessary.

Of course the most important thing is to be clear about the extent of your own responsibility, but you might also want to know who, in your area, allocates or investigates different kinds of cases, and who in the social services department has overall responsibility for child or adult protection.

If you want to expand this activity into one for your portfolio, obtain a copy of your local child or adult protection policy. Read it and note down the arrangements in your agency or local area in relation to either children or vulnerable adults. See if you can put names to roles, even if you have to do some detective work. This directory could then be annotated and put into your portfolio – it shows that you have a sound knowledge of the frameworks for addressing abuse in your local area.

Job Aid 2 – Responding to abuse in your area

When concerns arise about abuse of children or vulnerable adults, who in your agency/ area is responsible for:

- **alerting:** that is, passing on a concern to a senior person either inside or, if necessary, outside the 'alerter's' own establishment or agency.

  ....

  Add details if there is a special form you should use or a special number to call:

  ....

- **reporting**: that is, making an official record of the alert and triggering action under the procedures.

  First person to contact:

  ....

  Reserve, in case they do not take it seriously or are implicated in the abuse:

  ....

- **allocating the case**: who will decide what level of response is appropriate and which agency is best placed to lead the investigation?

  ....

- **investigating and assessment**: who will co-ordinate the gathering of information and the conduct of interviews, consulting other appropriate agencies to establish matters of fact and deciding how best to protect the child or vulnerable adult?

  ....

- **calling a case conference**: what are the 'rules' about conducting a case conference to decide what to do next and who else needs to know to keep this person safe and protect others who might be at risk? There may be guidelines in your local policy setting out when, as well as by whom, this should be convened and about who should attend.

  Who calls the conference? ....

  ....

  Within what time scale? ....

  ....

  Who should attend? ....

  ....

- **monitoring**: who needs to contribute to the collection of information about abuse cases in your area? You may need to fill in particular forms, enter particular codes on to the computer and/or produce figures which will be collated into an annual report.

  What information should I record? ....

  ....

  Is there a special form or computer code? ....

  ....

  Is there a regular report produced on abuse in our area? ....

  ....

You have now outlined the roles of the different people involved in responding to concerns about abuse. Passing on concerns through official channels is not designed to elicit a drastic or punitive response but one in which a balanced and holistic assessment is made, concerning a particular individual, family or establishment. If prior concerns have been raised these will be revisited and if evidence is needed it will be gathered using agreed procedures and safeguards. Making investigations alone in a 'Miss Marples' kind of way may make it more difficult to act appropriately later, for example through court proceedings, and it may jeopardise the possibility of taking action to keep someone safe or to restrict a perpetrator's access to vulnerable individuals.

2.5 Finishing the story

You have now completed the video activities. Like a Victorian novel I have spared you the worst excesses of the case, but here is the gist as it unfolded through the sequence of EastEnders episodes. Ruth's friend the social worker comes along and warns Ruth about overstepping the mark. She agrees to get involved herself 'unofficially' but then goes and talks to Adam's school, which is an extraordinary breach of confidentiality. Soon there is an irate Mrs Woods and an even more anxious Ruth, and eventually, in one of those 'making everything up over a cup of tea' scenes, which happen in soaps but unfortunately not in real life, Ruth and Mrs Woods become bosom pals!

 So what lay behind it all? If you view scene 10(j) you will find out.

So there you have it! Adam wasn't being abused but he did need help. A multidisciplinary assessment under 'official' child protection procedures might have arrived at the same conclusion with a lot fewer risks to all concerned. As it is, everyone in Walford has got to know about Adam's situation except social services. Ruth should be in deep trouble for overstepping the mark and breaching confidentiality. As for Mark, who shouldn't have been involved at all, he turned out to be the most sensible person in Walford and if I were in charge of Walford social services I think I just might headhunt him!

Ruth ends by saying that there are never any easy answers. You might well have some sympathy with her, but although the answers are rarely clear-cut, in this unit we have mapped out some clear channels for communication which Ruth has not accessed. You at least now know the importance of following agreed procedures when dealing with difficult behaviour, risk and potential abuse.

Having explored the Ruth and Adam situation so closely, it would be worth taking a quick look back at how Dev Sharma coped with assessing the risk to Arthur Durrant, following the 'knife incident' (Unit 4, pp. 192–6). You will see that he too was required to 'work in partnership' to assess risk and plan responses. Knowing what you do now, how well do you think he handled the situation? What else might he have done?

Section 3
Conclusion

In this unit you have explored the skills of managing boundaries and risk. You have seen that this involves being clear about your own and other people's roles and responsibilities, and working within agreed guidelines when you are relating to someone in a professional capacity. You have practised working within one framework for assessing difficult behaviour. When risk *is* identified, keeping accurate records and knowing your way around the system are both critical competences. Knowing who to share your concerns with and appreciating the limits of your role and expertise are also important.

Often services only get one chance to step in when an individual is being abused. Delicate judgments have to be made about when to confront the situation and about whether support or sanctions are most appropriate to the goal of protecting individuals and acting against exploiters or abusers. Good practice has evolved to ensure that no *one* person has to bear these responsibilities alone, but rather that clear and informed decisions are made together.

Managing risk is an unavoidable part of care work. This unit has allowed you to practise your skills and test your judgments, with all the luxury of hindsight and make-believe to shield you from the consequences of getting it wrong. In real life the only protection for vulnerable individuals and those who care for them comes in the form of shared working, agreed procedures and careful decision making.

This block has introduced you to these issues in relation to children and adults in families and residential care. You have learnt how to define abuse and to set a threshold beyond which you will intervene, using only formal channels of communication and decision making. You have also seen how intervention of this kind can support, as well as protect, individuals and families who are under pressure from personal and sexual violence and exploitation.

> If you are keeping a K100 portfolio, your work from Unit 25 can be added now.
>
> If you are building a VQ related portfolio, this is a good time to look at the VQ Pathways Guide.

Section 4
Study skills

4.1 Reading graphs

You have already done enough work on number skills in Block 6 so, rather than give you more work here, we suggest you go back over the study skills boxes in Unit 23 and make sure you understand them, particularly the two boxes on reading tables and graphs. Part C of TMA 06 is based on Figure 2 of Offprint 32.

4.2 Gearing up to revision

At the end of Block 5 you sketched a rough plan of the last weeks of the course, and marked where you hoped to find your main revision time. You also made a rough estimate of how many revision hours you hope to have overall. Perhaps you have already revisited this plan and begun to refine it. In any case, now is a good time to plan in more detail how you will use your time.

Activity 14

Allow about 45 minutes

A more detailed revision plan

(a)   To get yourself thinking strategically about your approach to revision, read Section 4 of Chapter 7 of *The Good Study Guide*.

(b)   Take a first stab at deciding which blocks of the course you are going to focus on in your revision. (Go back to the comments following Activity 15 in Unit 21 if you need to remind yourself about choosing blocks.)

(c)   Decide whether you will wait until you have finished Block 7 before starting your revision, or whether you will mix revision with studying this new material.

(d)   Decide roughly what percentage of your revision time you think you should give to:

- sorting out all your papers, files and materials
- going back over your chosen blocks
- rereading your essays
- practising sketching answers to questions, writing out timed answers, making up questions of your own
- group revision with one or more fellow students.

(e)   Work out roughly how many hours you have per block. Mark on your revision plan which days you hope to be doing what. (You may want to draw a fresh plan if the other one is a mess now.)

(f)   Mark down any tutorials, day schools or any other group revision sessions you have arranged.

Comment

(a)   You may find it useful to go back to this section of *The Good Study Guide* several times over the coming weeks, to remind yourself what you are trying to achieve.

(b)   You may change your mind about the blocks as you get back to them. But having an initial plan will help to force the issue about making strategic choices.

(c)   After TMA 06 there is no constraint on how you use your time up to the exam. It may make you feel more confident to begin some revising straight away. It will also help you to become realistic about what you can achieve in the time you have available. But *be sure not to put off Block 7 too late*, or there won't be time to absorb it before you have to write about it. Remember, it is the only block that is 'compulsory' in the exam, and it also includes advice on preparing for the exam.

(d)   Most people would choose to give the bulk of their time to block revision. But this reminds you to leave time for other modes of revision, which can be extremely helpful.

(e)   As the book says, it's very likely that you will have to change your plan as it is overtaken by events. But at least you will be in a position to readjust strategically, rather than simply muddle along.

(f)   Get as much support as you can from working with other people.

If you keep a strategic overview of your revision activities, you should find the coming weeks a very rewarding period of the course. As you look back and revive ideas which were in your mind months ago, and see the connections with what you've done since, you should begin to feel a growing confidence in your new knowledge and a deepening of your understanding. To help it turn out that way, here are two key principles to keep in mind.

- *Make revision meaningful and interesting.* Avoid letting it become boring. Seek out ways of making it active, enquiring, creative and varied.

- *Play to your strengths.* Build on your interests and experience. Work to patterns that suit you. Don't worry about what you're not – be yourself. You're doing this for you.

4.3 Developing your writing

As you approach your last TMA, it is time to review your writing skills. Do you feel you have made significant progress since February? And how do you feel in general now about the writing aspect of study?

Study skills: The intensity of writing

Do you look forward to writing, dread it, or simply resign yourself to it? Or is it a love/hate relationship – tremendously demanding, but also very rewarding to look back on? It would be quite surprising if it were something you treated lightly. Most people feel as if writing puts them through an emotional wringer. Why is this? And, as a student with perhaps several more years of writing ahead of you, can you cope with such intensity?

Activity 15

Allow about 30 minutes

Read Section 6, 'The experience of writing', in Chapter 6 of *The Good Study Guide*.

Then answer these questions. They correspond to the sub-sections of Section 6, so you may want to check back to the text as you think about them:

(a)   Do you sometimes feel that your writing makes you appear a bit stupid and inarticulate?

(b)   When you weigh up the quality of your writing, whose writing do you think you are comparing yourself against?

(c)   Do you feel frustrated by the gap between the ideas in your head and what you actually manage to put down on paper? Would you prefer it if nobody ever saw what you wrote?

(d)   Do you hesitate over reading your tutor's comments in detail? Do you sometimes feel bruised by them? Are you sometimes irritated by them? What are the three most important things you have learnt through your TMA relationship with your tutor?

(e)   •   Do you find the 'open-endedness' of writing makes you uncomfortable and restless? How does this affect your ability to keep at your writing?

•   Are you gradually finding it easier to 'position yourself' in relation to your imagined 'reader' – to find your 'voice'?

•   Do your essays seem rubbishy when you are about to send them off? Do they seem better when you read them a few months later?

•   Does the essay writing process seem to drag on far too long?

Comment

(a)   If it doesn't, you could make a fortune passing on the secret.

(b)   Have you managed to get a look at a few essays by other students this year? That's the best way of establishing a sensible point of comparison.

(c)   It helps if you can build a bridge between the private and the public, by getting into the habit of exchanging essays with one or two other people, so you get to feel less defensive about what you write and less sensitive about other people's comments. You could still usefully do this before the exam this year. But in any case you can look out for opportunities to do it next year.

(d)   I can assure you that the K100 authors experienced just these feelings when colleagues wrote comments all over drafts of units and then aired their views frankly at course team meetings. But we undoubtedly learnt a great deal from the process. Getting advice on writing seems to be one of those 'If it isn't hurting it isn't working' things (to quote John Major). I hope the pain led to progress for you too.

(e)   These are aspects of writing which remain problematic, however experienced you become. The point is to work out your own ways of 'managing' yourself, so that you can ride the problems rather than be thrown by them. I hope you feel you are making progress with all four.

Coming to terms with this 'personal' side of writing – the way it makes you feel about yourself and your abilities, the stresses and doubts it gives rise to – is as important as the conceptual and technical skills you have been developing throughout the year.

End of block assignment

Now TMA 06 presents you with one last exposure to the challenge of writing, and a final exchange in your 'relationship-through-writing' with your tutor. After all the experience and advice you have received this year and all you have read in *The Good Study Guide,* I hope you feel that you are approaching this essay with a lot more confidence, insight and technique than you brought to TMA 01.

Study skills: Study diary

Just a reminder to bring your study diary up to date, and help yourself to think ahead to Block 7.

References

Craft, A. and Brown, H. (1994) 'Personal relationships and sexuality: the staff role' in Craft, A. (ed.) *Practice Issues in Sexuality and Learning Disabilities*, Routledge, London, pp. 1–22.

Felce, D. and McBrien, J. (1991) *Challenging Behaviour and Severe Learning Difficulties*, First Draft Publications, BILD, Kidderminster.

Home Office in conjunction with the Department of Health (1992) *Memorandum of Good Practice: video-recorded interviews with child witnesses for criminal proceedings*, HMSO, London.

Acknowledgements

Grateful acknowledgement is made to the following sources for permission to reproduce material in this unit:

Illustrations

Pp. 192, 199 and 201: BBC.

Grateful acknowledgement is also made to the following sources for permission to reproduce the illustrations on the front cover of this book: all Sally and Richard Greenhill except *top right* Brenda Prince/Format and *bottom right* John Birdsall Photography.